THE
HIGH FIBRE
CALORIE-CONTROLLED
COOKBOOK

THE
HIGH FIBRE CALORIE-CONTROLLED
COOKBOOK

EDITED BY HELEN CHESTER

Ward Lock Limited · London

First published in revised form as
Cooking the New Diabetic Way.

First published in Great Britain in 1986
by Ward Lock Limited, 8 Clifford Street,
London W1X 1RB, an Egmont Company.

Designed by Niki fforde
Text filmset in Apollo
by MS Filmsetting Limited, Frome, Somerset

Printed and bound in Italy
by New Interlitho

British Library Cataloguing in Publication Data
The High fibre calorie-controlled Cookbook.
1. High-fibre diet—Recipes
641.5'637   RM237.6

ISBN 0-7063-6477-5

Notes
Recipe ingredients are given in both imperial
and metric measurements. You should follow
one system or the other. Mixing the two will
produce inferior results and will also make
the calorie calculations inaccurate.

Acknowledgements
Inside photography Eric Carter
Home Economist Roz Denny
Illustrations by Lorraine Calaora

The publisher would also like to thank
Harrods Ltd for kindly loaning
equipment for photography.

C·O·N·T·E·N·T·S

I·N·T·R·O·D·U·C·T·I·O·N

This book emphasizes a healthy approach to reduced calorie cooking – one that is low in fat and high in fibre. It will be a help to all slimmers and weight watchers, and to those family members who wish to enjoy healthy and interesting reduced calorie-controlled meals.

A sensible reduced calorie diet will help you lose weight and make you feel fitter, and is likely to result in a steady weight loss, plus, most importantly, maintenance of that lost weight.

Fats are the most concentrated source of calories we eat so that cutting down on them will result in very substantial savings. Additionally, the choice of foods that are rich in fibre ensures that meals are satisfying and filling – of particular importance on a reduced calorie diet and also whenever weight reduction must be maintained over a period of time.

LOSING WEIGHT

If you eat more calories than your body requires for its day-to-day demands, you will, over a period of time, become overweight. When you, therefore, decide to lose weight, it is essential that you cut back on your calorie intake. Many magazines and books feature charts which recommend a certain level of calorie intake related to one's age, height, weight and possibly level of day-to-day activity. Such charts are of very limited value because they fail to take into account the very real differences from one person to another in total food requirements and amounts actually eaten. The approach most recommended is to identify your current calorie intake so that a range of foods can be eaten that provide substantially less. In general, advice on calorie targets is best given by a State Registered Dietitian who will be able to recommend a safe and practical reduced calorie target. If it is not possible to arrange for a referral to a Dietitian via your General Practitioner or hospital doctor, then it is best to calculate your own calorie intake as indicated below rather than settling on levels propounded in various books and charts.

Calculating your previous diet

Keep a detailed record over a period of at least three days, (including at least one weekend day) of everything that you eat and drink. Use the Food Values Chart on pages 10–12, to calculate approximately how many calories you are currently consuming. You will probably find that there is some variation from day to day. Before deciding by how much to reduce the diet, add the totals from the number of days recorded, then divide this by the number of days used for the record. This will give you an indication of your average daily calorie intake on a day-to-day basis. In order to lose weight, you will generally need to reduce this quantity by about one-third. Most research has shown that by reducing your calories by about 500 each day, you are pretty well guaranteed to lose a minimum of $\frac{1}{2}$kg/1 lb a week, consistently, week after week. If you find that your previous calorie intake has been relatively low, ie less than 1200 calories, it is not wise to reduce your calorie intake below 1000 calories without seeking help from a Dietitian. He/she will need to check that your overall balance of nutrients, ie protein, minerals, trace elements and vitamins, is going to be adequate over a period of time.

Planning your meals

There is much evidence to suggest that it is best to take one's calorie needs spread across the whole day rather than to confine food intake to one or two particular meals or snacks. It is particularly important to ensure that you have some calories earlier in the day rather than the majority of your food late in the evening. As a rule, try to have two-thirds of your calorie target before 6pm.

In addition to the recipes in this book, try to make sure that any meals and accompaniments are low in fat and high in fibre. Do this by keeping meat portions below 75–100g/3–4 oz cooked weight, and choosing leaner meat where possible. Additionally, replace meat with fish or poultry on at least two days in any one week. Keep any spreading fats to the minimum; low-fat spreads are certainly recommended. Always use skimmed milk in your cooking, and try to use skimmed or semi-skimmed milk in any hot beverages, on breakfast cereals, etc. Have at least two or three root and/or green vegetables at each main meal. Even if you are having a sandwich or roll for lunch or tea, try to have a small portion of vegetables or salad with it.

To ensure that you are getting enough fibre in your diet, make sure that you have a high-fibre breakfast cereal or jacket potatoes/wholewheat pasta/brown rice/wholemeal bread/roll on at least two occasions during the day as part of your calorie allowance. Additionally, try to include butter beans, broad beans, sweetcorn etc, whenever possible, as one of your vegetables, and try to extend your meat portion by adding beans or lentils to a casserole, soup, etc.

If you like an alcoholic drink, there is no reason why you should not have one or two occasionally. But never have more than one drink for every thousand calories of your diet plan.

Finally, always try to sit down for meals. Do not eat "on the run". Sitting down increases the likelihood that you will feel fuller for a longer period of time so that you will not pick unsuitable foods later in the day.

Changing the calorie target
There are two reasons why you may need to change your calorie target:
1   You may have successfully lost any excess weight and do not wish to continue further weight reduction, but want to maintain weight. In this case, you will probably need to increase your calorie intake slightly by 100 or 200 calories per day. This usually maintains weight but you may need to reduce again or perhaps even increase after a period of weeks if your weight is not remaining stable. Once you have reached a stable state it will not be necessary to count calories so carefully. Do, however, be aware of the sorts of food that you have eaten to achieve your success, and try to maintain this approach. If on some days you have a little more than normal, then cut down over the next day or so to make amends. It makes sense to continue to check your weight, at least fortnightly, preferably at the same time of day.
2   You may have been unsuccessful in losing weight. In this case, it may well be that you have not been as accurate as you thought in counting the calories. You will, therefore, need at least a week or two on the same diet again, remembering, however, to check it very carefully. If you are not losing weight, this will be an indication that the calories need to be reduced further. If this might mean a diet containing less than 1000 calories, then you should definitely ask for referral to a local Dietitian.

For many people a slowing off in weight loss is reached after a couple of weeks or months but providing the diet is maintained, weight loss usually recommences. Sometimes it is even necessary to increase the diet slightly for a week or so before starting again. In any event, a Dietitian will be able to provide much help and support through what can be a difficult time.

About the recipes
The recipes in this book are created from basic everyday ingredients, and feature a broad range of tastes and flavours.

Each recipe clearly indicates its total calorie contribution, thereby enabling the user to select a range of recipes and portion sizes to fit in with his/her personal diet plan. The calories have been rounded up to the nearest 10 calories. The calculations are based on the metric version of the recipe, so that slimmers requiring complete accuracy should use the metric measurements.

The recipes are for either two or four average servings. If you prefer or need to have a larger or smaller portion of a particular recipe, divide the total calorie figure by the number of servings obtained from that recipe.

For example:

Mustard Pork and Mushrooms (page 48) has total calories 860. Divided into four equal servings, each portion contains 860 calories ÷ 4 = 215 calories
Divided into six smaller servings, each portion contains 860 ÷ 6 = 145 calories (approx).

The importance of reducing the fat in your cooking to a minimum cannot be overstressed. Every gram of fat you avoid saves nine calories. Save just 10 grams and you have saved 90 calories. When you are trying to keep to 1200 calories a day, 90 calories saved is no mean achievement. So follow carefully any instruction in a recipe to trim meat or to drain off any excess fat or oil.

4   Weights given for ingredients are for the food before any preparation has taken place, unless otherwise stated, eg *50g/2oz brown rice, cooked* implies 50g/2oz uncooked brown rice; but *50g/2oz cooked brown rice* implies exactly what is stated, ie 50g/2oz cooked weight. For the convenience of the cook, vegetables are often listed in the ingredients by size rather than weight. It is assumed that a small onion weighs about 50g/2oz, a medium onion, carrot or pepper weighs about 100g/4oz, and a large onion, carrot or pepper weighs about 225g/8oz. Where fresh fruit such as berries are indicated, the equivalent weight of frozen fruit can be substituted. Thaw and use as required.

5   Can or carton sizes are sometimes specified. Small variations from these standard sizes will not, however, make an appreciable difference to the success of the recipe or to the calculations.

6   Where herbs are used, these are dried, unless otherwise indicated.

7   A serving suggestion follows many recipes. In the case of main course dishes, this is designed to produce a well-balanced meal. If a recipe is quite high in calories, a low calorie acccompaniment is suggested. Similarly, if a recipe is not very rich in fibre, the recommended accompaniment makes up for this. Where vegetables are indicated, they should be cooked plainly, without fat. Of course, you may prefer to substitute your own ideas to fit in with your individual calorie or carbohydrate plan.

Note   The calorie and carbohydrate values of the foods contained in the serving suggestions have not been included in the recipe calculations.

8   Basic kitchen equipment is all that is required to follow the recipes. This must include accurate scales, a measuring jug and a set of standard measuring spoons. Frying pans, saucepans and baking tins should be non-stick so that a minimum amount of fat or oil may be used in cooking. In addition, a dry-fry pan, in which you can fry anything without adding oil or fat, is an excellent piece of equipment; a blender (liquidizer) is very useful for making soups and purées, although it is essential for only a very few recipes; and a pressure cooker saves a lot of cooking time, particularly for dried peas, beans and lentils.

9   A well stocked store cupboard and refrigerator will help you keep to your diet. The following is a list of foods which it is useful always to have in stock:

Dry and packaged goods
   Wholemeal or wholewheat flour, brown rice, wholewheat pasta, gelatine, a variety of dried fruit, dried peas, dried beans, lentils, stock cubes, Worcestershire sauce, cider or wine vinegar, lemon juice, sugar-free mixers and squashes, fructose (fruit sugar), liquid sweetener, dried herbs and spices

Canned foods
   Mackerel and tuna in brine, frankfurters in brine, tomatoes, sweetcorn, broad beans, butter beans, red kidney beans, tomato juice, concentrated tomato purée, canned fruit without added sugar

Refrigerated and frozen foods

A variety of seafood such as plain fish fillets, shrimps and prawns, frozen vegetables, good quality stewing beef, stewing lamb and "free-flow" mince, low fat margarine, skimmed milk, natural yoghurt

Prepared foods

A small supply of cold brown rice or wholewheat pasta is very useful to serve with salads and other cold dishes. Cook in the normal way, with any seasoning, then pour plenty of boiling water over the cooked rice or pasta, and drain well. Cover securely, and leave in a refrigerator for up to a week.

F·O·O·D V·A·L·U·E·S

The food values listed below feature ingredients used within the recipes in this book. If you wish to substitute an ingredient, choose one which contains the same calorie content.

INGREDIENT	AMOUNT	CALORIE CONTENT (approx)
Almonds, shelled	25g/1 oz	140
Apple, cooking (whole)	450g/1 lb	135
Apple, eating (whole)	450g/1 lb	160
Apple juice (unsweetened)	150ml/¼ pt	70
Apricots (canned in natural juice)	1 × 227g/8 oz can	100
Apricots (dried)	25g/1 oz	45
Apricots (fresh, whole)	450g/1 lb	125
Arrowroot	1 × 5ml spoon/1 teaspoon	20
Asparagus (fresh)	450g/1 lb	60
Asparagus tips (canned)	1 × 298g/10 oz can	45
Aubergine (whole)	450g/1 lb	50
Avocado pear (1 whole)	225g/8 oz	360
Bamboo shoots (canned)	1 × 285g/10 oz can	80
Banana (peeled)	50g/2 oz	40
Beans, adukie (dried)	25g/1 oz	60
Beans, broad (fresh or frozen)	25g/1 oz	15
Beans, butter (canned)	1 × 425g/15 oz can	280
Beans, green	25g/1 oz	5
Beans, red kidney (canned)	1 × 227g/8 oz can	165
Beans, red kidney (dried)	25g/1 oz	70
Beansprouts	450g/1 lb	50
Beef, minced (lean, raw)	450g/1 lb	800
Beef, stewing (lean, raw)	450g/1 lb	550
Biscuits, digestive (1 large)	15g/½ oz	70
Blackberries/blackcurrants (fresh or frozen)	450g/1 lb	120
Bread, wholemeal	1 large thin slice	70
Breadcrumbs, wholemeal (fresh)	25g/1 oz	55
Broccoli (fresh or frozen)	450g/1 lb	70

INGREDIENT	AMOUNT	CALORIE CONTENT (approx)
Cabbage, red (raw)	450g/1 lb	90
Cabbabe, white (raw)	450g/1 lb	100
Carrots (whole)	450g/1 lb	100
Cauliflower (whole)	450g/1 lb	40
Celery (raw)	450g/1 lb	25
Cheese, Cheddar	25g/1 oz	100–120
Cheese, cottage	25g/1 oz	25
Cheese, curd	25g/1 oz	50
Cheese, Edam	25g/1 oz	75
Cheese, Gouda	25g/1 oz	75
Cheese, Gruyère	25g/1 oz	100
Cheese, Mozzarella	25g/1 oz	100
Cheese, Parmesan	25g/1 oz	100
Cheese, quark	25g/1 oz	25
Cheese, ricotta	25g/1 oz	100
Chicken (cooked)	25g/1 oz	35
Chicken breast (raw)	450g/1 lb	540
Chicken leg (raw, whole)	1 × 225g/8 oz	200
Chick-peas (dried)	25g/1 oz	80
Chinese leaves	450g/1 lb	120
Cider (dry)	150ml/$\frac{1}{4}$ pint	55
Coconut (desiccated)	25g/1 oz	150
Cod fillet or steak (raw)	450g/1 lb	320
Cornflour	1 × 5ml spoon/1 teaspoon	20
Courgettes (whole)	450g/1 lb	100
Crabmeat (canned or frozen)	25g/1 oz	20
Cucumber (whole)	450g/1 lb	35
Currants	25g/1 oz	60
Custard powder	1 × 5ml spoon/1 teaspoon	20
Dates (pitted)	25g/1 oz	60
Egg (size 3)	1	80
Fennel (whole)	450g/1 lb	120
Flour (wholemeal/wholewheat)	25g/1 oz	80
Frankfurters (canned)	1 × 227g/8 oz can	550
Fructose (fruit sugar)	25g/1 oz	100
Gelatine	1 × 5ml spoon/1 teaspoon	15
Grapefruit (whole, unpeeled)	1 very large/400g/14 oz	45
Grapes (whole)	450g/1 lb	260
Haddock (fillet, raw)	450g/1 lb	330
Hake (fillet, raw)	450g/1 lb	330
Halibut (fillet, raw)	450g/1 lb	420
Ham (lean, cooked)	25g/1 oz	35–40
Lamb (lean, raw)	450g/1 lb	730
Leeks (whole)	450g/1 lb	50
Lentils (raw)	25g/1 oz	80
Lettuce	1 large	20
Liver, calf's	450g/1 lb	690
Liver, chicken	450g/1 lb	605
Liver, lamb's	450g/1 lb	800
Liver, pig's	450g/1 lb	690

INGREDIENT	AMOUNT	CALORIE CONTENT (approx)
Mackerel, smoked (fillets)	450g/1 lb	960
Mackerel, fresh (whole)	450g/1 lb	520
Mandarin oranges (canned in natural juice)	1 × 298g/10½ oz can	80
Mango (whole)	450g/1 lb	180
Margarine (low fat)	25g/1 oz	95
Marrow (whole)	450g/1 lb	40
Melon, cantaloupe (whole)	450g/1 lb	65
Melon, honeydew (whole)	450g/1 lb	55
Melon, water (whole)	450g/1 lb	50
Milk, skimmed (fresh)	550ml/1 pint	180
Mushrooms (raw)	225g/8 oz	35
Nuts, pecan (shelled)	25g/1 oz	195
Oatmeal	25g/1 oz	100
Oats, rolled	25g/1 oz	100
Oil, olive	1 × 15ml spoon/1 tablespoon	135
Oil, soya bean	1 × 15ml spoon/1 tablespoon	135
Oil, sunflower	1 × 15ml spoon/1 tablespoon	135
Oil, vegetable	1 × 15ml spoon/1 tablespoon	135
Olives, black (stoned)	25g/1 oz	25
Onion	450g/1 lb	100
Orange (whole)	1 large/150g/5 oz	40
Orange juice (concentrated, frozen)	1 × 180g/6¼ oz can	225
Pasta, wholewheat (raw)	25g/1 oz	80
Peaches (fresh whole)	1 large/125g/4½ oz	40
Pear (whole)	450g/1 lb	130
Peas (frozen cooked)	25g/1 oz	10
Peppers (whole)	450g/1 lb	60
Pineapple (canned in natural juice)	1 × 225g/8 oz can	130
Pineapple (fresh whole)	450g/1 lb	110
Pineapple juice (unsweetened)	150ml/¼ pint	75
Plaice, fillet (raw)	450g/1 lb	400
Plums, dessert (whole)	450g/1 lb	160
Pork cutlet (with bone)	450g/1 lb	1230
Pork fillet (raw)	450g/1 lb	660
Pork, minced (lean, raw)	450g/1 lb	660
Prawns (peeled)	25g/1 oz	30
Prunes (stoned)	25g/1 oz	40
Rabbit (raw)	450g/1 lb	560
Radishes	450g/1 lb	30
Raisins	25g/1 oz	60
Raspberries (raw)	450g/1 lb	110
Rhubarb (raw, prepared)	450g/1 lb	30
Rice, brown (raw)	25g/1 oz	95
Rice, brown flakes (raw)	25g/1 oz	90
Salmon (canned)	1 × 99g/3½ oz	155
Sauerkraut (canned or frozen)	450g/1 lb	80
Sherry, dry	150ml/¼ pint	170
Shredded wheat	1	80
Shrimps (canned)	1 × 113g/4 oz can	70
Shrimps (peeled)	25g/1 oz	30
Sole, lemon (fillet)	450g/1 lb	360
Strawberries (raw)	450g/1 lb	115

INGREDIENT	AMOUNT	CALORIE CONTENT (approx)
Sugar	25g/1 oz	100
Sultanas	25g/1 oz	60
Sunflower seeds	25g/1 oz	140
Sweetcorn (canned)	1 × 350g/12 oz can	280
Tofu (soya bean curd)	227g/8 oz pack	115
Tomatoes (canned)	1 × 400g/14 oz can	50
Tomatoes (fresh)	450g/1 lb	60
Tomato juice (unsweetened)	150ml/$\frac{1}{4}$ pint	25
Tomato purée	25g/1 oz	20
Tongue, ox (cooked)	25g/1 oz	60
Trout (whole)	450g/1 lb	220
Tuna (canned in brine)	1 × 200g/7 oz can	220
Turkey (fresh or frozen, meat only)	450g/1 lb	480
Veal escalope	450g/1 lb	490
Veal cutlet	1 medium 225g/8 oz	200
Veal fillet	450g/1 lb	490
Walnuts (shelled)	25g/1 oz	130
Water chestnuts (canned)	1 × 284g/10 oz can	110
Watercress	25g/1 oz	4
Wholewheat flake breakfast cereal	25g/1 oz	85
Wine, dry	150ml/$\frac{1}{4}$ pint	100
Yoghurt, natural (low fat)	1 small carton/150g/5.3 oz	80

S·O·U·P·S

A well-chosen soup can turn the most ordinary meal into an occasion. For slimmers, the vegetables also provide a very pleasant way of taking the edge off your appetite so you finish your main course quite satisfied and can resist the temptation of reaching for an unsuitable dessert.

A great advantage of soups is that they can be prepared in quantity and frozen, or kept for several days in a refrigerator. Why not keep a variety of soups in this way to ring the changes on your everyday diet?

Aubergine Soup

SERVES 2   *Total calories 180*

1 large aubergine, skinned and chopped
1 large onion, finely chopped
2 medium tomatoes, deseeded and
  chopped
1 medium green pepper, deseeded and
  chopped
2 cloves garlic, crushed
1 × 5ml spoon/1 teaspoon basil
275ml/½ pint cold water
1 chicken stock cube
150g/5.3 oz natural yoghurt (1 small
  carton)
salt, pepper

Garnish
fresh mint, chopped

Put the aubergine, onion, tomatoes, pepper, garlic and basil into a large saucepan, add the water and crumble in the stock cube. Heat slowly to boiling point, reduce the heat, cover and simmer for 30 minutes. Remove from the heat, cool slightly, then stir in the yoghurt. Season to taste, and garnish with chopped mint.

Celery and Fennel Soup

SERVES 2   *Total calories 80*

4 stalks celery, trimmed and chopped
½ head of fennel, trimmed and sliced
1 small onion, chopped
1 clove of garlic, crushed
salt, pepper
550ml/1 pint cold water
1 chicken stock cube

Garnish
paprika

Put the vegetables, garlic and seasoning into a large saucepan. Add the water and crumble in the stock cube. Heat to boiling point, reduce the heat, cover and simmer for 30 minutes. Season to taste, and garnish with paprika.

Chicken Soup

SERVES 2   *Total calories 280*

1 chicken leg
1 medium onion, chopped
2 large carrots, sliced
4 stalks celery, trimmed and chopped
salt, freshly ground black pepper
550ml/1 pint cold water
1 chicken stock cube

Put the chicken, vegetables and seasoning in a large saucepan. Add the water and crumble in the stock cube. Heat to boiling point, reduce the heat, cover and simmer for 1 hour. Cool slightly and remove the meat from the bone. Season to taste and sprinkle with freshly ground black pepper.

Cock-a-Leekie

SERVES 4   *Total calories 180*

225g/8 oz courgettes, sliced
450g/1 lb leeks, trimmed and sliced
1 large carrot, sliced
1 large onion, chopped
2 bay leaves
4 whole cloves
salt, freshly ground back pepper
550ml/1 pint cold water
1 chicken stock cube

Garnish
fresh parsley, chopped

Put the vegetables, bay leaves, cloves and seasoning in a saucepan. Add the water and crumble in the stock cube. Heat to boiling point, reduce the heat, cover and simmer for 45 minutes. Remove the bay leaves and cloves. Season to taste, and garnish with chopped parsley.

Cream of Celery Soup

SERVES 4   *Total calories 100*

1 large head of celery, trimmed and
   chopped
1 medium red pepper, deseeded and
   chopped
25g/1 oz fresh chives, chopped
550ml/1 pint water
1 chicken stock cube
150ml/$\frac{1}{4}$ pint skimmed milk
salt, pepper

Put the celery, pepper and chives into a saucepan, add the water and crumble in the stock cube. Heat to boiling point, reduce the heat, cover and simmer for 30 minutes. Sieve, or process in a blender for 2 minutes. Return to the saucepan and add the milk, then simmer for a further 10 minutes. Season to taste.

Serving suggestion Wholemeal toast

Country Soup

SERVES 4   *Total calories 340*

1 small onion, chopped
1 large leek, trimmed and sliced
225g/8 oz white cabbage, shredded
2 courgettes, finely sliced
2 large tomatoes, skinned and chopped
50g/2 oz brown rice
fresh parsley, chopped
1 × 2.5ml spoon/½ teaspoon basil
1 × 5ml spoon/1 teaspoon tarragon
3 whole cloves
2 cloves garlic, crushed
freshly ground black pepper
1 × 2.5ml spoon/½ teaspoon celery salt
1100ml/2 pints water
2 × 15ml spoons/2 tablespoons
    concentrated tomato pureé
1 beef stock cube

Put the vegetables, rice, herbs, cloves, garlic and seasoning in a large saucepan. Add the water and tomato pureé, and crumble in the stock cube. Heat to boiling point, reduce the heat, cover and simmer for 45 minutes. Leave to stand for 24 hours, then remove the cloves, reheat thoroughly and serve hot.

Cream of Courgette Soup

SERVES 4   *Total calories 100*

450g/1 lb courgettes, sliced
1 medium onion, chopped
1 clove of garlic, crushed
sprigs of parsley
550ml/1 pint water
1 beef stock cube
3 × 15ml spoons/3 tablespoons skimmed
    milk
salt, pepper
freshly ground black pepper

Put the courgettes, onion, garlic and parsley into a saucepan, add the water and crumble in the stock cube. Heat to boiling point, reduce the heat, cover and simmer for 15 minutes. Sieve, or process in a blender. Return to the pan and add the milk, then simmer for a further 10 minutes. Season to taste, and serve hot with a garnish of black pepper.

Country Soup

Leek and Chick-pea Soup

SERVES 4

Total calories 380

100g/4 oz chick-peas
450g/1 lb leeks, sliced
3 × 15ml spoons/3 tablespoons
    Worcestershire sauce
3 × 15ml spoons/3 tablespoons
    concentrated tomato pureé
salt, pepper
550ml/1 pint water
2 chicken stock cubes

Garnish
fresh parsley, chopped

Soak the chick-peas in water overnight. Put in a large saucepan with the leeks, Worcestershire sauce, tomato pureé and seasoning. Add the water, and crumble in the stock cubes. Heat to boiling point, reduce the heat, cover and simmer for $1\frac{1}{2}$ hours or until the chick-peas are tender. Alternatively, cook in a pressure cooker. Season to taste and garnish with chopped parsley.

Lettuce Soup

SERVES 2

Total calories 60

1 lettuce, shredded
1 medium onion, chopped
3 × 15ml spoons/3 tablespoons skimmed
    milk
1 clove of garlic, crushed
salt, pepper
550ml/1 pint cold water
1 chicken stock cube

Garnish
1 × 15ml spoon/1 tablespoon natural
    yoghurt

Put the lettuce, onion, milk, garlic and seasoning in a saucepan. Add the water and crumble in the stock cube. Heat to boiling point, reduce the heat, cover and simmer for 30 minutes. Season to taste and stir the yoghurt into the soup to garnish.

Thick Onion Soup

SERVES 4   *Total calories 320*

3 large onions, chopped
2 medium tomatoes, chopped
1 large carrot, sliced
2 bay leaves
nutmeg
550ml/1 pint cold water
4 × 15ml spoons/4 tablespoons dry white
   wine
1 beef stock cube
1 × 5ml spoon/1 teaspoon arrowroot
salt, pepper
25g/1 oz Parmesan cheese, grated

Put the onions, tomatoes, carrot, bay leaves and nutmeg into a saucepan. Add the water and wine, and crumble in the stock cube. Heat to boiling point, reduce the heat, cover and simmer for 30 minutes. Remove the bay leaves.

Mix the arrowroot with a little cold water and stir into the soup to thicken it slightly. Simmer for a further 10 minutes, then season to taste. Serve with the Parmesan cheese sprinkled on the top.

Vegetable Soup

SERVES 4   *Total calories 140*

4 stalks celery, trimmed and chopped
100g/4 oz white cabbage, finely chopped
225g/8 oz courgettes, sliced
1 medium red pepper, deseeded and
   chopped
275ml/½ pint tomato juice
550ml/1 pint cold water
fresh parsley, chopped
1 chicken stock cube
50g/2 oz button mushrooms, sliced
salt, pepper

Put the celery, cabbage, courgettes and pepper into a large saucepan, add the tomato juice, water and parsley, then crumble in the stock cube. Heat to boiling point, reduce the heat, cover and simmer for 45 minutes. Ten minutes before the end of the cooking time, add the mushrooms. Season to taste, and garnish with a little chopped parsley.

Gazpacho de España

SERVES 2

Total calories 200

550ml/1 pint tomato juice
1 clove of garlic, crushed
5 × 10ml spoons/5 dessertspoons wine
    vinegar
a pinch of basil
celery salt
freshly ground black pepper

Accompaniments
1 size 3 egg, hard-boiled and chopped
1 medium green pepper, deseeded and
    chopped
1 stalk of celery, trimmed and finely
    chopped
½ small cucumber, peeled and cubed

Sieve the tomato juice, garlic and vinegar or process in a blender. Season to taste and chill in a refrigerator before serving.

Put the egg, pepper, celery and cucumber in separate glass dishes and serve with the gazpacho.

Tomato Consommé

SERVES 2

Total calories 100

550ml/1 pint tomato juice
1 small onion, chopped
2 bay leaves
a pinch of basil
celery salt
white pepper
2 beef stock cubes

Put the tomato juice, onion, herbs and seasoning into a saucepan and crumble in the stock cubes. Heat to boiling point, reduce the heat, cover and simmer for 30 minutes. Remove the bay leaves, season to taste, cool, and then sieve, or process in a blender. Serve cold, or re-heat and serve hot.

Gazpacho de España

S·T·A·R·T·E·R·S

Many people feel that a starter is an obligatory part of a meal. The following selection is both low in fat and high in fibre.

Melon Cheese

SERVES 2

Total calories 200

450g/1 lb cantaloupe melon, skinned,
   deseeded and cubed
100g/4 oz cottage cheese
juice of 1 lemon
½ medium apple, cored and chopped
ground cinnamon

Mix together all the ingredients except the cinnamon. Chill in a refrigerator and sprinkle with cinnamon before serving.

Pecan Melon Starter

SERVES 2

Total calories 460

½ small honeydew melon, skinned,
   deseeded and cubed
150g/5.3 oz natural yoghurt (1 small
   carton)
50g/2 oz pecan nuts, chopped
1 × 5ml spoon/1 teaspoon curry powder
lettuce, shredded
Cayenne pepper

Mix together the melon, yoghurt, nuts and curry powder. Pile on to a bed of shredded lettuce and sprinkle with Cayenne pepper. Chill well before serving.

Asparagus Snack

SERVES 2   *Total calories 240*

50g/2 oz button mushrooms, sliced
6 asparagus tips
3 × 15ml spoons/3 tablespoons skimmed
   milk
salt, pepper
2 large thin slices wholemeal bread
25g/1 oz Edam cheese, grated

Garnish
tomato slices
fresh parsley, chopped

Put the mushrooms, asparagus tips, skimmed milk and seasoning in a saucepan and heat slowly for 10 minutes, stirring frequently.

Toast the bread and top with the mushroom and asparagus mixture. Sprinkle with the grated cheese, and grill for 2 minutes until melted. Garnish with the tomato slices and chopped parsley. Serve immediately.

Salmon Stuffed Eggs

SERVES 2   *Total calories 240*

2 size 3 eggs, hard-boiled
3 × 15ml spoons/3 tablespoons natural
   yoghurt
1 × 75g/3 oz can salmon, drained
fresh parsley, chopped
salt, pepper

Garnish
sprigs of parsley

Cut the eggs in half crossways and carefully remove the yolks. Mix the yoghurt, salmon and parsley, then season to taste. Use to fill the egg whites. Garnish with the sprigs of parsley.

Chilli Bean

SERVES 4   *Total calories 360*

75g/3 oz red kidney beans, dried *or*
   1 × 225g/8 oz can kidney beans,
   drained
1 small green pepper, deseeded and
   chopped
1 small red pepper, deseeded and
   chopped
2 fresh chillies, deseeded and sliced
1 × 5ml/1 teaspoon English mustard
   powder
1 × 15ml spoon/1 tablespoon wine
   vinegar
1 × 5ml spoon/1 teaspoon olive oil
1 × 5ml spoon/1 teaspoon yeast extract
a dash of Tabasco sauce
1 clove of garlic, crushed
3 × 15ml spoons/3 tablespoons water
salt, pepper

Garnish
watercress

Soak the dried kidney beans overnight in water. Drain well and discard the water. Put the beans in a pan with sufficient salted water, bring rapidly to the boil, and boil for 10 minutes. Reduce the heat, cover and simmer for a further 50 minutes. Alternatively, cook in a pressure cooker. Leave to cool, drain, then mix together with all the other ingredients. Serve in a large salad bowl and garnish with the watercress.

Chinese Mushrooms

SERVES 4   *Total calories 140*

450g/1 lb button mushrooms
225g/8 oz bamboo shoots
225g/8 oz beansprouts
2 medium onions, finely chopped
1 medium leek, trimmed and finely
   sliced
1 × 5ml spoon/1 teaspoon ground ginger
2 × 15ml spoons/2 tablespoons soy sauce
275ml/$\frac{1}{2}$ pint cold water
1 chicken stock cube

Garnish
fresh chives, chopped
fresh parsley, chopped

Put the vegetables, ginger and soy sauce in a casserole. Add the water and crumble in the stock cube. Cook at 180°C/350°F/Gas 4 for 25 minutes. Garnish with the chives and parsley, and serve hot.

Chilli Bean

Cocktail Crevette

SERVES 2   *Total calories 340*

100g/4 oz curd cheese
150g/5.3 oz natural yoghurt (1 small
   carton)
100g/4 oz peeled shrimps
25g/1 oz chives, chopped
1 × 5ml spoon/1 teaspoon curry powder
lettuce, shredded

Garnish
cucumber slices
paprika

Mix together the curd cheese, yoghurt, shrimps, chives and curry powder. Serve on a bed of shredded lettuce and garnish with the cucumber slices and a sprinkling of paprika.

Fish Salad

SERVES 4   *Total calories 280*

50g/2 oz crabmeat, flaked
50g/2 oz tuna fish, flaked
50g/2 oz salmon, flaked
50g/2 oz peeled prawns
6 stalks celery, trimmed and chopped
½ cucumber, peeled and cubed
100g/4 oz button mushrooms, sliced
juice of 1 lemon
1 × 5ml spoon/1 teaspoon celery salt
freshly ground black pepper

Garnish
lemon twists
tomato wedges

Mix together all the ingredients, and chill in a refrigerator for at least 2 hours before serving. Garnish with lemon twists and tomato wedges.

Hot Shrimp Savoury

SERVES 4   *Total calories 800*

225g/8 oz peeled shrimps
juice of 1 lemon
150g/5.3 oz natural yoghurt (1 small
  carton)
4 large thin slices wholemeal bread
2 size 3 eggs, separated
50g/2 oz Edam cheese, grated
salt, pepper

Garnish
watercress
thin tomato slices

Mix together the shrimps, lemon juice and yoghurt. Divide into four and use to cover each slice of bread. Whisk the egg whites until stiff, then fold in the cheese, and season to taste. Top each slice of bread with the mixture and cook at 190°C/375°F/Gas 5 for 20 minutes until the topping is golden-brown. Garnish with the watercress and tomato slices. Serve immediately.

Mackerel Pâté

SERVES 4   *Total calories 800*

200g/7 oz smoked mackerel fillets, flaked
150g/5.3 oz natural yoghurt (1 small
  carton)
75g/3 oz fresh wholemeal breadcrumbs
2 cloves garlic, crushed
juice of 1 lemon
freshly ground black pepper

Mix all the ingredients together to form a paste, or process in a blender until smooth. Serve in individual ramekin dishes.

Serving suggestion Any side salad

Calf's Liver Pâté

SERVES 4   *Total calories 580*

225g/8 oz calf's liver, chopped
1 small onion, finely chopped
2 cloves garlic, crushed
2 bay leaves
150ml/¼ pint cold water
1 chicken stock cube
salt, pepper
juice of ½ lemon
50g/2 oz curd cheese
50g/2 oz fresh wholemeal breadcrumbs

Garnish
fresh parsley, chopped

Put the liver, onion, garlic and bay leaves in a saucepan, add the water, crumble in the stock cube, and season to taste. Heat to boiling point, reduce the heat, and simmer for 20 minutes. Remove the bay leaves. Strain off the juice and stir in the lemon juice, curd cheese and breadcrumbs. Pour into small pots and chill in a refrigerator until set. Garnish with chopped parsley.

Serving suggestion Wholemeal toast

Seafood Cocktail

SERVES 4   *Total calories 200*

1 × 100g/4 oz can crabmeat, drained
1 × 100g/4 oz can shrimps, drained
6 green peppercorns, crushed
½ quantity of Tomato Sauce (page 76)
juice of 1 lemon

Garnish
shrimps
thin lemon slices

Mix together the crabmeat and shrimps. Add the crushed peppercorns to the tomato sauce and lemon juice, then mix with the seafood. Serve in glass dishes and garnish with a few shrimps and lemon slices.

Calf's Liver Pâté

Chicken Liver Pâté

SERVES 4

Total calories 340

175g/6 oz chicken livers
1 large onion, finely chopped
1 × 5ml spoon/1 teaspoon curry powder
150ml/¼ pint cold water
1 chicken stock cube
25g/1 oz fresh wholemeal breadcrumbs
juice of ½ lemon
salt, pepper

Garnish
lemon slices

Put the liver, onion, curry powder and water in a saucepan, and crumble in the stock cube. Heat to boiling point, reduce the heat, cover and simmer for 15 minutes. Leave to cool slightly. Mix in the breadcrumbs, lemon juice, salt and pepper, then process in a blender until smooth. Pour into small pots and leave to chill in a refrigerator. Garnish with slices of lemon.

Sauerkraut with Ham

SERVES 4

Total calories 460

350g/12 oz sauerkraut
175g/6 oz cooked lean ham, cubed
100g/4 oz green peas, cooked
1 × 200g/7 oz can sweetcorn, drained
1 medium red pepper, deseeded and
 chopped
1 × 15ml spoon/1 tablespoon wine
 vinegar
salt, pepper

Mix all the ingredients together well and chill in a refrigerator before serving.

F·I·S·H A·N·D S·H·E·L·L·F·I·S·H

Fish and shellfish make an ideal main course. Every bit as delicious as meat, both contain less fat and therefore less calories. They are also excellent value for money as they shrink very little during cooking.

The recipes given here use just a few types of fish and shellfish, all of which are easily obtainable everywhere. But fishmongers offer an enormous variety of species from which to choose and you will have great fun selecting from amongst the broad range available.

Casseroled Cod

SERVES 4   *Total calories 620*

675g/1½ lb cod fillet
3 medium onions, finely chopped
2 medium tomatoes, skinned and
    chopped
1 medium red pepper, deseeded and
    chopped
2 stalks celery, trimmed and chopped
juice of 1 lemon
2 × 15ml spoons/2 tablespoons
    Worcestershire sauce
3 × 15ml spoons/3 tablespoons cold water
1 bay leaf
fresh parsley
salt, pepper

Cut the fish into four pieces, and put into a casserole with the other ingredients. Cook at 190°C/375°F/Gas 5 for about 25 minutes.

Serving suggestion Jacket potatoes and spring greens

Slimmer's Fish Cakes

SERVES 2   *Total calories 340*

350g/12 oz cod fillet, cooked and skinned
1 medium onion, finely chopped
1 × 15ml spoon/1 tablespoon
   Worcestershire sauce
1 × 5ml spoon/1 teaspoon made French
   mustard
fresh parsley, chopped
salt, pepper
1 size 3 egg, well beaten
1 × 5ml spoon/1 teaspoon vegetable oil

Mix together all the ingredients except the oil. Form into four round cakes and flatten. Heat the oil in a non-stick frying pan and cook the fish cakes slowly for 10 minutes on each side.

Serving suggestion Wholemeal baps and baked beans

Haddock with Courgettes

SERVES 2   *Total calories 340*

350g/12 oz haddock fillet
juice of 1 lemon
450g/1 lb courgettes, sliced
150ml/$\frac{1}{4}$ pint fish stock (page 38)
1 × 2.5ml spoon/$\frac{1}{2}$ teaspoon dill seeds
1 × 2.5ml spoon/$\frac{1}{2}$ teaspoon fennel
1 × 2.5ml spoon/$\frac{1}{2}$ teaspoon parsley
salt, pepper

Garnish
2 × 15ml spoons/2 tablespoons canned
   sweetcorn

Divide the fish into two portions and put in a casserole. Add the remaining ingredients and cook at 190°C/375°F/Gas 5 for 20 minutes. Garnish with the sweetcorn.

Serving suggestion Whole new potatoes and runner beans

Hake with Cheese

SERVES 2   *Total calories 250*

1 lemon, sliced
225g/8 oz hake fillet
freshly ground black pepper
25g/1 oz Edam cheese, grated

Garnish
paprika

Put the lemon slices on the fish, sprinkle with pepper, and wrap in foil. Put the parcel on a baking tray and cook at 180°C/350°F/Gas 4 for 20 minutes. Remove the lemon slices, sprinkle with the cheese and place under a hot grill until the cheese melts. Garnish with a sprinkling of paprika.

Serving suggestion Jacket potatoes and grilled tomatoes

Cidered Mackerel

SERVES 2   *Total calories 560*

2 small whole mackerel, ready gutted
juice of 1 lemon
1 large onion, finely chopped
1 bay leaf
salt, pepper
150ml/¼ pint dry cider

Garnish
fresh parsley, chopped

Accompaniment
stewed apple

Place the mackerel in a casserole with all the other ingredients and cook at 160°C/325°F/Gas 3 for 1 hour. Remove the bay leaf, garnish with chopped parsley and serve with a little stewed apple.

Serving suggestion Jacket potatoes and broccoli

Baked Tuna with Broccoli

SERVES 4

Total calories 540

1 × 200g/7 oz can tuna in brine, drained
1 × 200g/7 oz can sweetcorn, drained
salt, pepper
225g/8 oz broccoli, broken into florets
150ml/¼ pint tomato juice
25g/1 oz Gouda cheese, grated
25g/1 oz fresh wholemeal breadcrumbs
1 × 5ml spoon/1 teaspoon oregano

Flake the tuna and put in an ovenproof dish. Cover with the sweetcorn, season and then cover with broccoli. Pour the tomato juice over the fish and vegetables. Mix together the cheese, breadcrumbs and oregano, and sprinkle on the fish to form a topping. Cook at 190°C/375°F/Gas 5 for about 25 minutes.

Serving suggestion Jacket potatoes and mixed vegetables

Crunchy Tuna Ring

SERVES 4

Total calories 400

2 × 15ml spoons/2 tablespoons water
3 × 5ml spoons/3 teaspoons gelatine
1 × 200g/7 oz can tuna in brine, drained
½ small cucumber, peeled and cubed
½ medium red pepper, deseeded and
  chopped
1 small onion, finely chopped
6 small gherkins, chopped
2 large tomatoes, skinned and chopped
1 × 15ml spoon/1 tablespoon low calorie
  salad cream
150g/5.3 oz natural yoghurt (1 small
  carton)
salt, pepper

Garnish
cucumber slices
tomato slices

Put the water in a heatproof container, sprinkle in the gelatine and leave to soften. Stand the container in a pan of hot water and stir until the gelatine dissolves. Leave to cool. Mix together the remaining ingredients and fold in the gelatine. Pour into a 550ml/1 pint ring mould and leave in a refrigerator until set. This will take about 2 hours. Remove from the ring mould and garnish with slices of cucumber and tomato.

Serving suggestion Whole new potatoes and sweetcorn

Tarragon Sole

SERVES 2

Total calories 320

50g/2 oz button mushrooms
1 small onion, finely chopped
1 medium green pepper, deseeded and
   finely chopped
1 × 15ml spoon/1 tablespoon wine
   vinegar
150ml/¼ pint water
tarragon
parsley
salt, pepper
2 whole lemon sole, ready gutted
   (175g – 225g/6 – 8 oz each)

Garnish
lemon wedges
tomato wedges

Put the vegetables, vinegar, water, herbs, salt and pepper into an ovenproof dish. Place the fish, whole, on top and cover with foil. Cook at 180°C/350°F/Gas 4 for 25 minutes. Put the fish on a serving dish, drain the vegetables and arrange them around the fish. Garnish with lemon and tomato wedges.

Serving suggestion Jacket potatoes and sweetcorn

Marinated Tuna

SERVES 2

Total calories 320

1 × 200g/7 oz can tuna in brine, drained
1 medium tomato, skinned and chopped
1 medium apple, cored and chopped
50g/2 oz button mushrooms, sliced
1 medium onion, finely chopped
2 × 15ml spoons/2 tablespoons wine
   vinegar
1 clove of garlic, crushed
1 × 2.5ml spoon/½ teaspoon dill seeds
juice of ½ lemon
salt, pepper

Mix all the ingredients together well and marinate for at least 2 hours before serving.

Serving suggestion Cold brown rice and any side salad

Party Fish Platter

SERVES 2

Total calories 320

350g/12 oz fillet of plaice
2 × 5ml spoons/2 teaspoons water
1 × 5ml spoon/1 teaspoon tarragon
salt, pepper
4 black olives

Garnish
thin lemon slices
fresh parsley, chopped

Divide the fillet into two strips. Roll up each piece with the skin on the inside and secure with cocktail sticks. Put in an ovenproof dish with the water, tarragon, salt and pepper. Cover with foil and bake at 160°C/325°F/Gas 3 for about 20 minutes. Leave to cool completely. Place on a serving dish with an olive at either end of each fillet. Garnish with lemon slices and chopped parsley.

Serving suggestion Cold brown rice and bean salad

Salmon and Egg Mousse

SERVES 4

Total calories 900

2 × 15ml spoons/2 tablespoons water
3 × 5ml spoons/3 teaspoons gelatine
1 × 200g/7 oz can salmon, drained
3 size 3 eggs, hard-boiled and finely
    chopped
2 medium tomatoes, skinned and
    chopped
1 × 350g/12 oz can sweetcorn, drained
150g/5.3 oz natural yoghurt (1 small
    carton)
fresh parsley, chopped
1 × 5ml spoon/1 teaspoon celery salt
freshly ground black pepper

Garnish
cucumber slices

Put the water in a heatproof container, sprinkle in the gelatine and leave to soften. Stand the container in a pan of hot water and stir until the gelatine dissolves. Leave to cool, then mix with the remaining ingredients. Pour into a 550ml/1 pint mould and leave in a refrigerator until set. This will take about 2 hours. Remove from the mould, and garnish with cucumber slices.

Serving suggestion Whole new potatoes and any side salad

Salmon and Egg Mousse

Banana Trout

SERVES 2

Total calories 300

150ml/¼ pint fish stock
2 × 15ml spoons/2 tablespoons dry white
  wine
1 medium onion, finely chopped
50g/2 oz fennel, chopped
juice of ½ lemon
white pepper
2 trout, ready gutted (150g/5 oz each)

Garnish
1 small banana, sliced

Put all the ingredients except the fish in a saucepan. Heat to boiling point, reduce the heat, cover and simmer for 15 minutes, add the fish and cook for a further 10 minutes. Drain, and place the trout on a serving dish. Garnish with slices of banana.

Serving suggestion Creamed potatoes and broccoli

Fish Stock

Total calories NEG

550ml/1 pint water
fish bones
1 × 5ml spoon/1 teaspoon tarragon
1 × 5ml spoon/1 teaspoon mixed dried
  herbs
1 clove of garlic
1 bay leaf
freshly ground black pepper
a slice of lemon

Put all the ingredients in a large saucepan, heat to boiling point, reduce the heat, cover and simmer for 30 minutes. Pass through a sieve and season to taste. Use as required.

Cold Seafood Medley

SERVES 4   *Total calories 500*

175g/6 oz peeled shrimps
1 × 200g/7 oz can tuna in brine, drained
175g/6 oz cod fillet, cooked and flaked
100g/4 oz button mushrooms, sliced
6 radishes, sliced
juice of 1 lemon
½ quantity of Yoghurt Dressing (page 77)
salt, pepper

Garnish
paprika

Carefully mix together the shrimps, tuna and cod, the mushrooms, radishes and lemon juice. Fold in the yoghurt dressing and season to taste. Chill in a refrigerator and sprinkle with paprika before serving.

Serving suggestion Wholemeal baps and any side salad

Shrimps in Garlic Sauce

SERVES 4   *Total calories 480*

1 × 5ml spoon/1 teaspoon vegetable oil
1 medium onion, finely chopped
3 cloves garlic, crushed
1 × 5ml spoon/1 teaspoon concentrated
    tomato purée
6 × 15ml spoons/6 tablespoons water
1 × 5ml spoon/1 teaspoon oregano
freshly ground black pepper
350g/12 oz peeled shrimps

Heat the oil in a non-stick frying pan and add the onion, garlic and tomato purée. Cook gently for 5 minutes and then add the water, oregano, black pepper and the shrimps. Cook gently for a further 10 minutes and serve immediately.

Serving suggestion Brown rice and whole French beans

Prawns with Asparagus

SERVES 2   *Total calories 200*

100g/4 oz peeled prawns
100g/4 oz whole French beans
1 medium tomato, skinned and chopped
1 × 175g/6 oz can asparagus tips, drained
juice of ½ lemon
½ quantity of Yoghurt Dressing (page 77)
lettuce
freshly ground black pepper

Mix together the prawns, beans, tomato, asparagus and lemon juice. Gently fold in the yoghurt dressing. Chill in a refrigerator and serve on a bed of crispy lettuce. Sprinkle with freshly ground black pepper.

Serving suggestion Whole new potatoes and sweetcorn

Pepper Prawns

SERVES 2   *Total calories 480*

1 × 5ml spoon/1 teaspoon vegetable oil
1 medium onion, finely chopped
1 clove of garlic, crushed
1 medium green pepper, deseeded and
   chopped
225g/8 oz peeled prawns
150ml/¼ pint tomato juice
1 × 2.5ml spoon/½ teaspoon celery salt
1 × 2.5ml spoon/½ teaspoon fennel
1 × 2.5ml spoon/½ teaspoon black pepper
4 × 15ml spoons/4 tablespoons dry white
   wine
50g/2 oz dried apricots, chopped

Heat the oil gently in a non-stick saucepan. Cook the onion, garlic and pepper for about 10 minutes until soft. Stir in the remaining ingredients, cover and simmer gently for a further 10 minutes. Sprinkle with freshly ground black pepper and serve immediately.

Serving suggestion Wholewheat pasta shells or noodles and whole green beans

Pepper Prawns

M·E·A·T

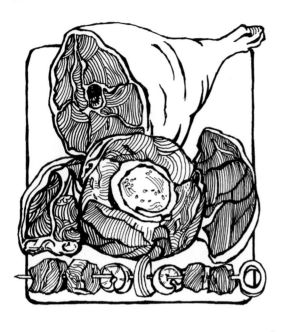

It would be hard for most of us to imagine a diet which did not include meat. But, as they are concentrated sources of calories, the slimmer must get used to eating smaller quantities. You can, however, compensate for this by adding more vegetables, thereby satisfying both your diet sheet and your appetite.

To keep the calories down, fat is hardly ever added in the cooking and you should be sure always to trim the meat and skim the stock as thoroughly as possible.

Beef with Gherkin Sauce

SERVES 2   *Total calories 500*

225g/8 oz lean stewing beef, trimmed and cubed
1 medium onion, finely chopped
1 medium carrot, sliced
1 celery stalk, trimmed and chopped
150ml/¼ pint water
salt, pepper
1 × 5ml spoon/1 teaspoon mixed herbs
8 small gherkins
1 beef stock cube
150g/5.3 oz natural yoghurt (1 small carton)
25g/1 oz curd cheese

Garnish
chopped gherkins

Put the beef, onion, carrot, celery, water, seasoning, mixed herbs and gherkins in a large saucepan. Crumble in the stock cube. Heat slowly to boiling point, reduce the heat, cover and simmer for 1 hour. Cool slightly, season to taste and stir in the yoghurt and curd cheese. Serve immediately, garnished with chopped gherkins.

Serving suggestion Brown rice and green beans

Rich Beef Casserole

SERVES 4   *Total calories 560*

1 × 5ml spoon/1 teaspoon vegetable oil
275g/10 oz stewing beef, trimmed and
    cubed
1 × 15ml spoon/1 tablespoon
    concentrated tomato purée
2 medium carrots, sliced
2 medium onions, sliced
2 medium tomatoes, chopped
275ml/$\frac{1}{2}$ pint water
2 cloves garlic, crushed
fresh parsley, chopped
1 beef stock cube
salt, pepper

Heat the oil in a non-stick frying pan and add the beef, turning it carefully to seal all sides. Stir in the tomato purée, and add the vegetables. Heat to boiling point, and then transfer to a casserole. Add the water, garlic and parsley, crumble in the stock cube, and season to taste. Cook at 190°C/375°F/Gas 5 for 1 hour.

Serving suggestion Jacket potatoes and spring greens

Sweet and Sour Meatballs

SERVES 4   *Total calories 960*

350g/12 oz lean minced beef
1 small onion
75g/3 oz fresh wholemeal breadcrumbs
salt, pepper
1 size 3 egg, well beaten
150ml/$\frac{1}{4}$ pint water
1 beef stock cube
2 stalks celery, trimmed and chopped
1 medium carrot, finely sliced
1 small leek, finely sliced
1 medium onion, trimmed and finely
    chopped
4 × 15ml spoons/4 tablespoons vinegar
2 × 15ml spoons/2 tablespoons
    concentrated tomato purée
2 × 15ml spoons/2 tablespoons soy sauce
liquid sweetener

Mix together the minced beef, onion, breadcrumbs, salt and pepper, and bind together with the beaten egg. Form the mixture into small balls. Put the remaining ingredients, except the liquid sweetener, in a saucepan, heat to boiling point, reduce the heat, cover and simmer for a further 15 minutes. Season to taste, add the sweetener, and serve immediately.

Serving suggestion Wholewheat ribbon noodles and broccoli

Indian Lamb Kebabs

SERVES 4   *Total calories 860*

1 × 5ml spoon/1 teaspoon turmeric
1 × 5ml spoon/1 teaspoon paprika
1 × 5ml spoon/1 teaspoon celery salt
2 × 5ml spoons/2 teaspoons vegetable oil
4 × 15ml spoons/4 tablespoons wine
   vinegar
juice of 1 lemon
2 bay leaves
liquid sweetener
450g/1 lb fillet of lamb, cut into
   2.5cm/1 inch cubes
100g/4 oz button mushrooms

Garnish
tomato slices
watercress

Put the turmeric, paprika, celery salt, vinegar, lemon juice, bay leaves and the liquid sweetener in a bowl and mix well. Add the lamb, and marinate for 4 hours, turning from time to time.

Thread the meat on to long skewers, alternating with the mushrooms. Grill for about 10 minutes on each side, until well browned and cooked through, brushing several times with the marinade. Garnish with tomatoes and watercress.

Serving suggestion Brown rice and any mixed salad

Ragoût of Lamb

SERVES 4   *Total calories 860*

1 clove of garlic
450g/1 lb lean stewing lamb, cubed
2 medium onions, finely chopped
1 × 2.5ml spoon/½ teaspoon rosemary
1 × 2.5ml spoon/½ teaspoon basil
salt, pepper
275ml/½ pint water
1 chicken stock cube
175g/6 oz broad beans, lightly cooked

Rub the garlic over the lamb. Mix together the lamb, onions and herbs, season to taste, and leave to stand for 30 minutes in a casserole. Add the water, crumble in the stock cube, and cook at 200°C/400°F/Gas 6 for 1 hour. Five minutes before serving, stir in the broad beans.

Serving suggestion Jacket potatoes and mixed vegetables

Indian Lamb Kebabs

Hot Lamb Curry

SERVES 4

Total calories 1100

2 × 5ml spoons/2 teaspoons vegetable oil
450g/1 lb lean lamb, cut into small cubes
3 medium onions, chopped
2 cloves garlic, crushed
25g/1 oz lentils
1 × 5ml spoon/1 teaspoon curry paste
1 × 5ml spoon/1 teaspoon Cayenne
   pepper
1 × 2.5ml spoon/½ teaspoon cardamon
1 × 2.5ml spoon/½ teaspoon coriander
   seeds
1 × 2.5ml spoon/½ teaspoon cinnamon
25g/1 oz fresh root ginger
150ml/¼ pint water
juice of 1 lemon
1 chicken stock cube
100g/4 oz frozen peas
salt, pepper
150g/5.3 oz natural yoghurt (1 small
   carton)

Garnish
lemon slices

Heat the oil in a non-stick saucepan and add the lamb, turning it carefully to seal all sides. Add the onions and garlic and cook until the onion is soft. Stir in the lentils and spices, then add the water and lemon juice, and crumble in the stock cube. Heat to boiling point, reduce the heat, cover and simmer for 1 hour. Add the peas and remove the piece of ginger 5 minutes before serving. Season to taste, and stir in the yoghurt. Serve garnished with lemon slices.

Serving suggestion Brown rice and any side salad

Calf's Liver with Fennel

SERVES 2

Total calories 440

1 bulb of fennel, trimmed and sliced
1 medium green pepper, deseeded and
   chopped
100g/4 oz mushrooms, sliced
150ml/¼ pint water
salt, pepper
2 × 5ml spoons/2 teaspoons mixed herbs
1 clove of garlic, crushed
1 chicken stock cube
225g/8 oz calf's liver, sliced
juice of ½ lemon

Put the vegetables in a large saucepan. Add the water, seasoning, herbs and garlic, and crumble in the stock cube. Heat to boiling point, reduce the heat, cover and simmer for 20 minutes. Dip the liver in the lemon juice and grill for 8 minutes on each side. Transfer to a serving dish and cover with the vegetables. Serve immediately.

Veal Casserole

SERVES 2   *Total calories 400*

225g/8 oz stewing veal, cubed
2 medium onions, finely chopped
2 medium green peppers, deseeded and
  chopped
225g/8 oz mushrooms, sliced
275ml/½ pint tomato juice
1 clove of garlic, crushed
1 × 15ml spoon/1 tablespoon soy sauce
1 × 5ml spoon/1 teaspoon oregano
salt, pepper
225g/8 oz whole green beans

Put all the ingredients except for the green beans in a casserole. Cook at 190°C/375°F/Gas 5 for 1 hour. Add the green beans and cook for a further 15 minutes. Serve hot.

Veal Cutlets with Mushroom Sauce

SERVES 2   *Total calories 500*

100g/4 oz button mushrooms
12 button onions
1 × 5ml spoon/1 teaspoon basil
1 × 5ml spoon/1 teaspoon celery salt
1 × 5ml spoon/1 teaspoon black pepper
275ml/½ pint water
1 chicken stock cube
2 veal cutlets (175g/6 oz each approx)
150g/5.3 oz natural yoghurt (1 small
  carton)
1 × 15ml spoon/1 tablespoon
  Worcestershire sauce

Garnish
fresh parsley, chopped

Put the mushrooms, onions, basil, celery salt and pepper in a saucepan, add the water and crumble in the stock cube. Heat to boiling point, reduce the heat, cover and simmer for 10 minutes. Put the veal cutlets into the stock and simmer for a further 15 minutes, turning from time to time. When cooked, stir in the yoghurt and Worcestershire sauce. Serve immediately with a garnish of chopped parsley.

Serving suggestion Whole new potatoes and spinach

Mustard Pork and Mushrooms

SERVES 4   *Total calories 860*

1 × 15ml spoon/1 tablespoon made
   English mustard
2 × 15ml spoons/2 tablespoons
   concentrated tomato purée
350g/12 oz lean pork fillet, cubed
1 × 425g/15 oz can butter beans, drained
150ml/¼ pint tomato juice
100g/4 oz button mushrooms, sliced
1 × 2.5ml spoon/½ teaspoon rosemary
1 × 2.5ml spoon/½ teaspoon thyme
1 × 2.5ml spoon/½ teaspoon garlic salt
1 × 2.5ml spoon/½ teaspoon black pepper

Mix together the mustard and tomato purée, and use to coat the pork. Place in an ovenproof dish. Add the remaining ingredients, cover with foil, seal well and cook at 190°C/375°F/Gas 5 for 40 minutes.

Serving suggestion Jacket potatoes and green peas

Pork Rissoles

SERVES 2   *Total calories 320*

175g/6 oz lean pork, minced
25g/1 oz fresh wholemeal breadcrumbs
1 × 5ml spoon/1 teaspoon made French
   mustard
1 × 5ml spoon/1 teaspoon concentrated
   tomato purée
1 clove of garlic, crushed
salt, pepper

Garnish
fresh parsley, chopped
tomato slices

Mix all the ingredients together well, and form into two rissoles. Grill under a medium heat for 10 minutes on each side. Garnish with chopped parsley and tomato slices.

Serving suggestion Green salad and wholemeal rolls

Pork Rissoles

American Club Salad

Total calories 600

100g/4 oz cooked chicken, chopped
100g/4 oz lean cooked ham, chopped
100g/4 oz cooked tongue, chopped
1 × 225g/8 oz can bamboo shoots, drained
1 lettuce
1 small cucumber, peeled and cubed
1 medium green pepper, deseeded and
　chopped
1 clove of garlic, crushed
½ quantity of Vinaigrette (page 77)
salt, pepper

Garnish
thin tomato slices
fresh parsley, chopped

Put all the ingredients in a large salad bowl and mix together well. Garnish with thin slices of tomato and chopped parsley.

P·O·U·L·T·R·Y A·N·D G·A·M·E

Poultry and game are an excellent alternative to beef, pork and lamb because they are naturally lower in fat. This means that portions can usually be slightly more generous. Additionally, if chosen regularly, the slimmer can be certain of keeping the level of fat in his/her reduced calorie diet down to a healthy minimum.

Chicken Chasseur

SERVES 4   *Total calories 880*

4 medium carrots, sliced
2 medium onions, sliced
225g/8 oz button mushrooms, sliced
275ml/½ pint tomato juice
2 cloves garlic, crushed
150ml/¼ pint water
1 × 5ml spoon/1 teaspoon basil
salt, pepper
1 chicken stock cube
4 chicken breasts, skinned and boned
75g/3 oz sweetcorn
150g/5.3 oz natural yoghurt (1 small
  carton)

Put the carrots, onions, mushrooms, tomato juice and garlic in a large casserole. Add the water, basil and seasoning, and crumble in the stock cube. Cook at 180°C/350°F/Gas 4 for 45 minutes. Add the chicken pieces and sweetcorn and cook for a further 30 minutes. Place the chicken on a hot serving dish. Stir the yoghurt into the sauce in the casserole, then pour it over the chicken and serve immediately.

Serving suggestion Jacket potatoes and green peas

Marinated Chicken Casserole

SERVES 4   *Total calories 700*

4 chicken breasts, skinned and boned
275ml/½ pint cold water
juice of 1 lemon
1 chicken stock cube
1 × 15ml spoon/1 tablespoon sunflower
　oil
2 medium onions, sliced
1 medium green pepper, deseeded and
　sliced
100g/4 oz button mushrooms, sliced
1 × 5ml spoon/1 teaspoon celery salt
1 × 5ml spoon/1 teaspoon paprika
1 × 5ml spoon/1 teaspoon coriander seeds
freshly ground black pepper

Put the chicken breasts, water and lemon juice in a casserole. Crumble in the stock cube, and marinate for two hours. Heat the oil in a frying pan and gently cook the onions, pepper and mushrooms until tender. Add the celery salt, paprika, coriander seeds and pepper to taste, and cook for a further 2 minutes. Put the vegetable mixture into the casserole and cook at 190°C/375°F/Gas 5 for 30 minutes.

Serving suggestion Jacket potatoes and green peas

Pineapple Chicken

SERVES 2   *Total calories 380*

2 chicken breasts, skinned and boned
150ml/¼ pint pineapple juice
2 slices canned pineapple in natural
　juice, chopped
2 × 15ml spoons/2 tablespoons dry white
　wine
1 × 2.5ml spoon/½ teaspoon garlic salt
freshly ground black pepper

Garnish
sprigs of watercress
tomato slices

Put all the ingredients in a casserole, cover and leave in a refrigerator to marinate overnight. Cook at 180°C/350°F/Gas 4 for 30 minutes. Garnish with watercress and tomato slices.

Marinated Chicken Casserole (opposite), Cucumber and Celery Crunch (page 70)
and Fruit Yoghurt Dessert (page 83)

Chicken Paprika

SERVES 4

Total calories 480

4 small chicken legs, skinned
2 × 5ml spoons/2 teaspoons paprika
150ml/$\frac{1}{4}$ pint water
1 chicken stock cube
1 small onion, finely chopped
1 medium red pepper, deseeded and
    chopped
1 medium green pepper, deseeded and
    chopped
1 clove of garlic, crushed
salt, pepper

Garnish
paprika

Put all the ingredients in a casserole and cook at 200°C/400°F/Gas 6 for 40 minutes. Place the chicken in a serving dish and pour over the liquid. Garnish with a sprinkling of paprika.

Serving suggestion Jacket potatoes and sweetcorn

Citrus Chicken

SERVES 2

Total calories 440

225g/8 oz cooked chicken, diced
75ml/$\frac{1}{8}$ pint unsweetened orange juice
juie and grated rind of 1 lemon
1 medium onion, chopped
1 medium red pepper, deseeded and
    chopped
thyme
salt, pepper
225g/8 oz white cabbage, shredded
soy sauce

Put the chicken in a saucepan with the orange juice, lemon rind, onion, red pepper and thyme. Season to taste, and simmer for 15 minutes. Fold the cabbage into the chicken mixture, cover and cook for a further 2 minutes. Serve immediately with soy sauce.

Serving suggestion Brown rice and mixed vegetables

Coq au Vin

4 chicken breasts, skinned and boned
150ml/¼ pint dry white wine
100g/4 oz button mushrooms, sliced
1 medium carrot, sliced
1 medium onion, chopped
1 × 5ml spoon/1 teaspoon oregano
salt, pepper
150ml/¼ pint water
1 chicken stock cube

Garnish
fresh parsley, chopped

Put the chicken, wine, vegetables, oregano, salt and pepper in a large casserole. Add the water and crumble in the stock cube. Cook at 180°C/350°F/Gas 4 for 40 minutes. Serve with a garnish of chopped parsley.

Garlic Chicken Salad

175g/6 oz cooked chicken, diced
½ quantity of Vinaigrette (page 77)
1 medium apple, cored and sliced
1 medium onion, finely chopped
2 cloves garlic, crushed
salt, pepper
fresh beansprouts

Put the chicken in the vinaigrette dressing and marinate for 2 hours. Add the remaining ingredients, and mix well. Serve on a bed of fresh beansprouts.

Sherry Chicken

SERVES 2   *Total calories 460*

2 chicken breasts, skinned and boned
juice of 2 lemons and grated rind of 1
  lemon
1 × 5ml spoon/1 teaspoon vegetable oil
1 medium carrot, sliced
3 medium onions, chopped
1 medium red pepper, deseeded and
  chopped
225g/8 oz white cabbage, shredded
2 × 15ml spoons/2 tablespoons dry
  sherry
2 × 15ml spoons/2 tablespoons wine
  vinegar
1 × 5ml spoon/1 teaspoon ground ginger
salt, pepper

Garnish
fresh chives, chopped

Flatten out the chicken breasts with a rolling-pin.
Sprinkle with half the lemon juice and leave to stand
for 1 hour. Heat the oil in a pan and gently cook the
carrot, onions, pepper and cabbage until soft. Stir in
the sherry, vinegar, remaining lemon juice, lemon
rind, ginger, salt and pepper, and cook for a further
2 minutes. Place the chicken in an ovenproof dish
and cook at 190°C/375°F/Gas 5 for 30 minutes.
Garnish with chopped chives.

Serving suggestion Whole new potatoes and whole
green beans

Turkey Courgettes

SERVES 2   *Total calories 420*

225g/8 oz turkey, cubed
450g/1 lb courgettes, sliced
1 × 15ml spoon/1 tablespoon tomato juice
2 × 15ml spoons/2 tablespoons
  Worcestershire sauce
150ml/¼ pint water
1 chicken stock cube
1 medium onion, finely chopped
2 × 5ml spoons/2 teaspoons mixed herbs

Garnish
fresh parsley, chopped

Put all the ingredients in a casserole and cook at
190°C/375°F/Gas 5 for 30 minutes. Garnish with
chopped parsley and serve immediately.

Serving suggestion Whole new potatoes and spinach

56

Turkey Seconds

SERVES 2

Total calories 400

2 medium onions, chopped
100g/4 oz button mushrooms
25g/1 oz fresh parsley, chopped
½ small cucumber, peeled and cubed
juice of 1 lemon
150ml/¼ pint water
1 chicken stock cube
225g/8 oz cooked turkey, finely chopped
1 × 15ml spoon/1 tablespoon skimmed
  milk
1 × 5ml spoon/1 teaspoon celery salt
pepper

Garnish
fresh mushrooms, chopped

Put the onions, mushrooms, parsley, cucumber and lemon juice in a saucepan. Add the water and crumble in the stock cube. Heat to boiling point, reduce the heat, cover and simmer for 10 minutes. Add the turkey and simmer for a further 20 minutes. Remove from the heat, then add the milk and salt and pepper to taste. Serve with a garnish of chopped mushrooms.

Serving suggestion Brown rice and green peas

Chinatown Rabbit

SERVES 4

Total calories 820

450g/1 lb rabbit meat, cubed
450g/1 lb beansprouts
225g/8 oz bamboo shoots, chopped
3 medium onions, finely chopped
225g/8 oz whole French green beans
225g/8 oz white cabbage, finely shredded
275ml/½ pint water
2 × 15ml spoons/2 tablespoons
  Worcestershire sauce
1 × 15ml spoon/1 tablespoon
  concentrated tomato purée
2 cloves garlic, crushed
2 × 5ml spoons/2 teaspoons oregano
salt, pepper
1 chicken stock cube

Mix together the meat and vegetables. Add the water, Worcestershire sauce, tomato purée, garlic, oregano, salt and pepper, then crumble in the stock cube. Mix well and put in a casserole. Cook at 180°C/350°F/Gas 4 for 40 minutes. Serve with a dash of soy sauce.

Serving suggestion Brown rice and cauliflower

Spicy Rabbit

SERVES 2

Total calories 400

225g/8 oz rabbit meat, minced
1 large onion, finely chopped
2 medium tomatoes, skinned and
   chopped
1 medium green pepper, deseeded and
   chopped
1 medium red pepper, deseeded and
   chopped
150ml/$\frac{1}{4}$ pint water
1 chicken stock cube
1 clove of garlic, crushed
1 × 2.5ml spoon/$\frac{1}{2}$ teaspoon rosemary
1 × 2.5ml spoon/$\frac{1}{2}$ teaspoon ground
   ginger
1 × 2.5ml spoon/$\frac{1}{2}$ teaspoon cinnamon
salt, pepper

Garnish
nutmeg

Mix all the ingredients together well and put in a casserole. Cook at 190°C/375°F/ Gas 5 for 25 minutes. Transfer to a serving dish, sprinkle with nutmeg and serve immediately.

Serving suggestion Brown rice and carrots

V·E·G·E·T·A·R·I·A·N D·I·S·H·E·S

It makes good economic and slimming sense to include a few dishes without meat in your weekly diet, and the recipes in this chapter show just how easy it is to prepare interesting and satisfying vegetable dishes.

The main-course salads which follow present new ways of approaching salads guaranteed to enliven any diet.

Mushroom Bake

SERVES 2   *Total calories 260*

225g/8 oz button mushrooms, sliced
100g/4 oz cottage cheese
25g/1 oz Parmesan cheese, grated
2 medium onions, finely chopped
juice of $\frac{1}{2}$ lemon
salt, pepper

Garnish
sprigs of parsley
lemon wedges

Put the mushrooms in an ovenproof dish. Mix together the cottage cheese, Parmesan cheese, onions, lemon juice, salt and pepper, then spread the mixture over the mushrooms. Cook at 190°C/375°F/Gas 5 for 30 minutes. Garnish with sprigs of parsley and lemon wedges, and serve immediately.

Serving suggestion Jacket potatoes, and carrots and peas

Baked Rice and Tomato

SERVES 2

Total calories 480

100g/4 oz brown rice
1 × 5ml spoon/1 teaspoon vegetable oil
1 medium onion, finely chopped
1 clove of garlic, crushed
275ml/½ pint water
1 × 5ml spoon/1 teaspoon oregano
1 × 5ml spoon/1 teaspoon basil
2 large tomatoes, chopped
salt, pepper
1 beef stock cube

Put the rice in a pan of boiling salted water and cook for about 25 minutes. Drain and rinse, then put in an ovenproof dish. Heat the oil in a saucepan and cook the onion and garlic gently for 5 minutes until soft. Add the water, herbs, tomato and seasoning, and crumble in the stock cube. Mix with the rice and cook at 180°C/350°F/Gas 4 for 25 minutes.

Serving suggestion Any pulse salad

Slimmer's Hamburgers

SERVES 4

Total calories 360

75g/3 oz chick-peas
2 medium carrots, finely chopped
2 medium onions, finely chopped
1 medium green pepper, deseeded and
  finely chopped
2 stalks celery, trimmed and finely
  chopped
1 × 2.5ml spoon/½ teaspoon parsley
1 × 2.5ml spoon/½ teaspoon thyme
1 × 2.5ml spoon/½ teaspoon celery salt
freshly ground black pepper
2 size 3 eggs, well beaten

Garnish
onion rings
lettuce

Soak the chick-peas in water overnight. Put in a saucepan with sufficient salted water, and heat to boiling point. Reduce the heat, cover and simmer for 1 hour. Alternatively, cook the chick-peas in a pressure cooker.

Steam the vegetables with the herbs and seasoning for about 15 minutes until tender.

Mash the chick-peas, and mix together with the vegetables and the beaten egg. Form into four patties, and cook in a fairly hot oven, 190°C/375°F/Gas 5 for 30 minutes. Garnish with onion rings and lettuce.

Serving suggestion Wholemeal baps and any side salad

Slimmer's Hamburgers

Cauliflower Cheese

SERVES 4   *Total calories 760*

1 large cauliflower, trimmed and cut into
   quarters
25g/1 oz low fat spread
25g/1 oz wholemeal/wholewheat flour
550ml/1 pint skimmed milk
1 × 5ml spoon/1 teaspoon dry English
   mustard
1 × 5ml spoon/1 teaspoon celery salt
freshly ground black pepper
100g/4 oz Edam cheese, grated

Cook the cauliflower in boiling salted water for about 15 minutes. Melt the low fat spread in a saucepan and stir in the wholemeal flour. Cook for 3 minutes, stirring all the time. Remove from the heat and stir in the milk, mustard, celery salt and black pepper. Stir in the cheese and continue to stir until it melts. Pour over the cooked cauliflower and sprinkle with freshly ground black pepper.

Serving suggestion Whole French beans

Cheese and Onion Crumble

SERVES 2   *Total calories 320*

1 small onion, finely chopped
50g/2 oz Edam cheese, grated
50g/2 oz fresh wholemeal breadcrumbs
150ml/$\frac{1}{4}$ pint skimmed milk
salt, pepper
paprika

Garnish
tomato slices

Cover the base of an ovenproof dish with the onion. Mix together the cheese, breadcrumbs, skimmed milk, salt and pepper, and spread the mixture over the onions. Sprinkle with paprika. Cook at 230°C/450°F/Gas 8 for 10 minutes, then garnish with tomato slices, and serve immediately.

Serving suggestion Jacket potatoes and sweetcorn

Cheese-topped Oat and Aubergine

SERVES 4   *Total calories 900*

50g/2 oz oatmeal
2 medium aubergines
1 × 5ml spoon/1 teaspoon vegetable oil
2 medium onions, finely chopped
175g/6 oz mushrooms, chopped
1 × 5ml spoon/1 teaspoon chervil
1 × 5ml spoon/1 teaspoon oregano
1 clove of garlic, crushed
salt, pepper
175g/6 oz Gruyère cheese, grated

Pour boiling water over the oatmeal and leave to stand overnight. Prick the skins of the aubergines with a fork, and bake at 190°C/375°F/Gas 5 for 20 minutes. Leave to cool, then scoop out the flesh. Gently heat the oil and sauté the onions and mushrooms until soft, then add the herbs, garlic, salt and pepper. Drain the oatmeal and mix with the vegetables. Pour onto an ovenproof dish and cover with the cheese. Cook at 190°C/375°F/Gas 5 for 20 minutes.

Serving suggestion Any side salad

Cheese Meringue

SERVES 2   *Total calories 400*

4 size 3 eggs, separated
4 × 15ml spoons/4 tablespoons natural
  yoghurt
25g/1 oz Edam cheese, grated
freshly ground black pepper

Whisk the egg whites until stiff and pour into an ovenproof dish. Make four small dents in the whites and add the yolks. Cover the yolks with the yoghurt, and sprinkle with the grated cheese. Cook at 180°C/350°F/Gas 4 for 20 minutes, then sprinkle with black pepper and serve immediately.

Serving suggestion Whole new potatoes and runner beans

Adukie Bean Salad

SERVES 2   *Total calories 280*

100g/4 oz adukie beans
juice of $\frac{1}{2}$ lemon
1 medium onion, chopped
1 medium red pepper, deseeded and
    chopped
2 cloves garlic, crushed
salt, pepper
$\frac{1}{2}$ quantity of Vinaigrette (page 77)

Soak the beans overnight in water. Drain well and discard the water. Put the beans in a pan with sufficient salted water, bring rapidly to the boil and boil for 10 minutes. Add the lemon juice, reduce the heat, cover and simmer for 1 hour. Alternatively, cook the beans in a pressure cooker. Rinse the cooked beans in cold water, drain, and leave to cool. Mix with the other ingredients, and leave to stand for at least 2 hours before serving.

Serving suggestion Cottage cheese

Wholewheat Pasta Salad

SERVES 4   *Total calories 400*

100g/4 oz wholewheat pasta, eg shells *or*
    macaroni
2 medium carrots, sliced
1 medium green pepper, deseeded and
    chopped
4 stalks celery, trimmed and chopped
1 × 2.5ml spoon/$\frac{1}{2}$ teaspoon garlic powder
1 × 15ml spoon/1 tablespoon
    Worcestershire sauce

Garnish
fresh parsley, chopped

Put the pasta in a pan of boiling salted water and cook for 15 – 20 minutes. Drain, and leave until cool. Mix with the remaining ingredients, and garnish with chopped parsley.

Wholewheat Pasta Salad

Oatmeal Salad

SERVES 4

Total calories 480

50g/2 oz coarse oatmeal
225g/8 oz cottage cheese
1 small onion, sliced
1 medium apple, cored and sliced
1 medium red pepper, deseeded and
    chopped
25g/1 oz fresh parsley, chopped
salt, freshly ground black pepper
ground nutmeg
cress

Pour boiling water over the oatmeal and leave to stand overnight. Mix together all the remaining ingredients, except the cress, add to the oatmeal, and mix well. Chill in a refrigerator, and serve on a bed of cress.

Sunflower Rice Salad

SERVES 4

Total calories 400

50g/2 oz brown rice
1 × 5ml spoon/1 teaspoon turmeric
25g/1 oz sunflower seeds
2 medium onions, chopped
½ medium red pepper, deseeded and
    chopped
½ fresh chilli, deseeded and chopped
1 clove of garlic, crushed
fresh parsley, chopped
salt, pepper
½ quantity of Vinaigrette (page 77)

Put the rice and turmeric in a saucepan of boiling salted water and cook for about 45 minutes. Drain and rinse the rice. Leave to cool, then mix together with the sunflower seeds, onions, pepper, chilli, garlic, parsley and seasoning. Pour over the vinaigrette dressing. Leave to stand for 2 hours before serving.

V·E·G·E·T·A·B·L·E·S, S·I·D·E S·A·L·A·D·S, S·A·U·C·E·S A·N·D D·R·E·S·S·I·N·G·S

Cooked vegetables or side salads add bulk, fibre, vitamins and minerals to your diet, but very few calories. They are, therefore, important accompaniments to your main course dish.

Sauces and dressings are designed to help you add exciting flavours to your food, without adding extra calories. They enliven the taste-buds and enrich many recipes. Each one given here will keep well in a refrigerator for several days, so can be prepared ahead and used with a variety of dishes.

Bouquet of Vegetables

SERVES 4   *Total calories 200*

100g/4 oz green peas, cooked
100g/4 oz whole runner beans, cooked
100g/4 oz mushrooms, sliced
$\frac{1}{2}$ small cucumber, cubed
1 large onion, chopped
100g/4 oz radishes, sliced
100g/4 oz cauliflower, broken into florets
1 medium red pepper, deseeded and
    chopped
1 × 5ml spoon/1 teaspoon celery salt
1 clove of garlic, crushed
freshly ground black pepper
150ml/$\frac{1}{4}$ pint tomato juice

Mix all the vegetables and seasoning together in a large salad bowl. Pour in the tomato juice, and marinate for 12 hours before serving.

Serving suggestion Any cold meat

Caraway Cabbage

SERVES 4   *Total calories 260*

450g/1 lb white cabbage, finely shredded
450g/1 lb cooking apples, peeled, cored
   and sliced
juice of 1 lemon
1 × 5ml spoon/1 teaspoon caraway seeds
2 × 15ml spoons/2 tablespoons currants
   or raisins

Mix the cabbage and apple together in a large salad bowl. Add the lemon juice, caraway seeds and dried fruit, and leave to stand for at least 2 hours before serving.

Festive Mushrooms

SERVES 2   *Total calories 110*

3 × 15ml spoons/3 tablespoons white
   wine vinegar
2 cloves
2 sticks cinnamon
225g/8 oz button mushrooms, sliced
150g/5.3 oz natural yoghurt (1 small
   carton)

Garnish
red pepper, chopped

Put the vinegar, cloves and cinnamon sticks in a saucepan. Heat to boiling point, reduce the heat, cover and simmer for 5 minutes. Add the mushrooms to the liquid and simmer for a further 10 minutes, with the lid off the pan, until the liquid has evaporated. Place on a serving dish, cover with the yoghurt and garnish with chopped red pepper.

German Red Cabbage

SERVES 4   *Total calories 200*

450g/1 lb red cabbage, finely shredded
450g/1 lb cooking apples, cored and
   chopped
275ml/½ pint cold water
3 × 15ml spoons/3 tablespoons wine
   vinegar
salt, pepper

Put the cabbage and apples in a large saucepan, and add the water, vinegar and seasoning. Heat to boiling point, reduce the heat, cover and simmer for 20 minutes. Drain well, and serve hot or cold.

Serving suggestion Sliced lean meats

Marrow Casserole

SERVES 2

Total calories 160

1 small marrow, deseeded and sliced
1 medium red pepper, deseeded and
    sliced
2 medium courgettes, sliced
2 medium tomatoes, sliced
2 cloves garlic, crushed
150ml/¼ pint tomato juice
1 × 5ml spoon/1 teaspoon basil
1 × 5ml spoon/1 teaspoon oregano
salt, pepper

Put all the ingredients in a large casserole. Cook at 190°C/375°F/Gas 5 for 45 minutes. Serve hot.

Serving suggestion Jacket potatoes and any lean oven-baked chop

Beansprout Salad

SERVES 4

Total calories 360

175g/6 oz beansprouts
1 × 200g/7 oz can sweetcorn, drained
4 stalks celery, trimmed and chopped
175g/6 oz button mushrooms
50g/2 oz lentils, cooked
juice of 1 lemon
1 × 15ml spoon/1 tablespoon wine
    vinegar
salt, black pepper

Garnish
fresh mint

MIx all the ingredients together in a large salad bowl. Chill in a refrigerator, and garnish with fresh mint.

Chinese Leaf and Pepper Salad

SERVES 4

Total calories 60

225g/8 oz Chinese leaves, chopped
1 medium onion, chopped
1 medium green pepper, deseeded and
   chopped
6 radishes, sliced
1 × 2.5ml spoon/½ teaspoon celery salt
freshly ground black pepper
½ quantity of Vinaigrette (page 77)

Put the vegetables in a large salad bowl. Add the seasoning, and pour on the vinaigrette dressing. Marinate for 2 hours before serving.

Crispy Chicory Salad

SERVES 4

Total calories 340

2 large oranges, chopped
225g/8 oz cottage cheese
fresh parsley, chopped
salt, pepper
½ quantity of Vinaigrette (page 77)
350g/12 oz chicory, chopped
Cayenne pepper

Mix together the orange pieces, cottage cheese, parsley, salt, pepper and vinaigrette dressing. Put the chicory on to a serving dish, make a well in the centre, and fill with the cottage cheese mixture. Chill in a refrigerator and sprinkle with Cayenne pepper before serving.

Cucumber and Celery Crunch

SERVES 4

Total calories 120

1 medium cucumber, cubed
2 medium onions, finely chopped
1 medium green pepper, deseeded and
   chopped
4 stalks celery, trimmed and chopped
juice of 1 lemon
1 × 15ml spoon/1 tablespoon wine
   vinegar
1 × 5ml spoon/1 teaspoon celery salt
1 × 5ml spoon/1 teaspoon mixed herbs
freshly ground black pepper

Put the vegetables in a salad bowl, and add the lemon juice, vinegar, celery salt, herbs and pepper. Mix well together, and chill in a refrigerator before serving.

Curried Rice Salad

SERVES 2   *Total calories 250*

50g/2 oz brown rice, cooked
2 medium onions, chopped
2 cloves garlic, crushed
2 × 5ml spoons/2 teaspoons curry
    powder
1 × 5ml spoon/1 teaspoon cinnamon
salt, pepper

Put the rice and onions into a bowl. Add the garlic and spices, mix well together and season to taste.

Serving suggestion Cold meats or sliced hard-boiled eggs

Water Chestnut Salad

SERVES 4   *Total calories 180*

1 × 275g/10 oz can water chestnuts,
    drained and sliced
225g/8 oz beansprouts, chopped
1 medium onion, finely chopped
1 medium red pepper, deseeded and
    chopped
2 medium tomatoes, chopped
2 × 15ml spoons/2 tablespoons lemon
    juice
1 × 15ml spoon/1 tablespoon soy sauce
2 cloves garlic, crushed
salt, pepper
½ quantity of Vinaigrette (page 77)

Put the water chestnuts and vegetables in a large salad bowl, add the lemon juice, soy sauce, garlic and seasoning. Mix well together. Pour on the vinaigrette dressing and marinate for 2 hours before serving.

Garden Salad

SERVES 4

Total calories 120

juice of 1 lemon
3 × 15ml spoons/3 tablespoons wine
    vinegar
150ml/¼ pint water
salt, pepper
3 × 5ml spoons/3 teaspoons gelatine
1 medium carrot, grated
1 medium red-skinned apple, cored and
    grated
1 medium onion, chopped
2 medium tomatoes, chopped
2 stalks celery, trimmed and chopped

Garnish
radish roses
sprigs of watercress

Mix together in a heatproof container the lemon juice, vinegar, water, seasoning and gelatine. Leave until the gelatine softens, then stand the container in a pan of hot water and stir until the gelatine dissolves. Fill a glass bowl with separate layers of carrot, apple, onion, tomatoes and celery. Pour over the gelatine mixture and leave in a refrigerator until set. Turn out of the dish and garnish with radish roses and sprigs of watercress.

Apple Vinaigrette

Total calories 80

150ml/¼ pint white wine vinegar
juice of 1 lemon
1 × 5ml spoon/1 teaspoon made French
    mustard
150ml/¼ pint unsweetened apple juice
1 × 2.5ml spoon/½ teaspoon celery salt
1 clove of garlic, crushed
1 small carrot, grated
salt, pepper

Put the vinegar, lemon juice, mustard, apple juice and celery salt through a sieve, or process in a blender. Pour into a screw-topped jar and add the garlic, carrot and seasoning.

Garden Salad

Caraway Dressing

Total calories NEG

150ml/¼ pint wine vinegar
1 clove of garlic, crushed
1 × 2.5ml spoon/½ teaspoon caraway
  seeds
1 × 5ml spoon/1 teaspoon chives,
  chopped
1 × 5ml spoon/1 teaspoon made French
  mustard
salt, pepper

Mix all the ingredients together well, and leave to stand for at least 6 hours before serving.

Cucumber and Onion Raita

Total calories 140

½ small cucumber, chopped
1 medium onion, chopped
150g/5.3 oz natural yoghurt (1 small
  carton)
1 × 5ml spoon/1 teaspoon curry powder
salt, pepper

Garnish
paprika

Mix all the ingredients together well. Sprinkle with paprika and chill in a refrigerator. Serve with curries and other spicy dishes.

Cucumber Sauce

Total calories 25

½ small cucumber, peeled and chopped
150ml/¼ pint wine vinegar
salt, pepper

Mix together the ingredients, then sieve, or process in a blender. Serve with white fish.

Horseradish and Yoghurt Dressing

Total calories 80

150g/5.3 oz natural yoghurt (1 small
   carton)
2 × 15ml spoons/2 tablespoons
   horseradish, finely grated
salt, pepper

Mix together the yoghurt and horseradish, and
season to taste. Serve with cold meats.

Mock Mayonnaise

Total calories 180

100g/4 oz cottage cheese
1 × 15ml spoon/1 tablespoon wine
   vinegar
1 × 5ml spoon/1 teaspoon made French
   mustard
juice of $\frac{1}{2}$ lemon
150g/5.3 oz natural yoghurt (1 small
   carton)
1 × 2.5ml spoon/$\frac{1}{2}$ teaspoon garlic salt
1 × 2.5ml spoon/$\frac{1}{2}$ teaspoon celery salt
freshly ground black pepper

Mix all the ingredients together well, and sieve, or
process in a blender. Pour into a screw-topped jar.

Note This mayonnaise needs to be stirred well
before using a second time.

Slim Salad Sauce

Total calories 60

275ml/½ pint tomato juice
2 × 15ml spoons/2 tablespoons wine
    vinegar
½ small green pepper, deseeded and
    chopped
salt, pepper
1 × 2.5ml spoon/½ teaspoon garlic powder
1 × 5ml spoon/1 teaspoon made English
    mustard
1 × 15ml spoon/1 tablespoon
    Worcestershire sauce

Put all the ingredients in a saucepan. Heat to boiling point, reduce the heat, cover and simmer for 30 minutes. Season to taste, and pour into a serving jug. Serve hot or cold with meat and poultry.

Tartare Sauce

Total calories 80

150g/5.3 oz natural yoghurt (1 small
    carton)
1 × 15ml spoon/1 tablespoon wine
    vinegar
1 × 5ml spoon/1 teaspoon chives,
    chopped
1 × 5ml spoon/1 teaspoon capers,
    chopped
salt, pepper

Mix all the ingredients together well, and serve with fish.

Tomato Sauce

Total calories 100

1 × 400g/14 oz can tomatoes
2 medium onions, finely chopped
2 cloves garlic, crushed
2 × 15ml spoons/2 tablespoons vinegar
1 × 2.5ml spoon/½ teaspoon oregano
1 × 2.5ml spoon/½ teaspoon basil
1 × 2.5ml spoon/½ teaspoon coriander
salt, pepper

Put all the ingredients in a large saucepan. Heat to boiling point, reduce the heat, cover and simmer for 45 minutes. Sieve, or process in a blender. Leave to stand for 24 hours before serving. Season to taste, and use cold as a salad dressing, or re-heat and serve hot.

Yoghurt Dressing

Total calories 80

150g/5.3 oz natural yoghurt (1 small carton)
1 × 5ml spoon/1 teaspoon made French mustard
2 × 15ml spoons/2 tablespoons wine vinegar
juice of 1 lemon
salt, pepper

Mix all the ingredients together well, and serve with fish, eggs or cold chicken.

Sauce Provençale

Total calories 110

150g/5.3 oz natural yoghurt (1 small carton)
2 × 15ml spoons/2 tablespoons wine vinegar
4 × 15ml spoons/4 tablespoons concentrated tomato purée
1 clove of garlic, crushed
1 × 2.5ml spoon/$\frac{1}{2}$ teaspoon thyme
salt, pepper

Mix all the ingredients together well, and serve cold with fish or cold chicken.

Vinaigrette

Total calories NEG

150ml/$\frac{1}{4}$ pint wine vinegar
juice of 1 lemon
salt, pepper

Mix all the ingredients together well, and use for any green salad.

P·U·D·D·I·N·G·S AND D·E·S·S·E·R·T·S

As few people can resist the occasional old-fashioned pudding or rich dessert, a number of recipes based on these have been included. These combine ingredients which are relatively low in calories to produce unusual flavours and textures. Although their fat content has been kept to a minimum, none are low enough in calories to be eaten in quantity.

Date Crumble

SERVES 4   *Total calories 660*

100g/4 oz pitted dried dates
3 × 15ml spoons/3 tablespoons cold water
100g/4 oz rolled oats
juice of 1 large lemon
1 × 5ml spoon/1 teaspoon grated nutmeg

Put the dates in a saucepan with the water and cook gently for about 5 minutes. Place in a small oven-proof dish and cover with the rolled oats. Sprinkle the lemon juice and nutmeg over the top and bake at 190°C/375°F/Gas 5 for 25 minutes. Serve hot.

Lemon and Apricot Flan

SERVES 4–8

Total calories 740

100g/4 oz dried apricots
100g/4 oz wholemeal/wholewheat flour
50g/2 oz low fat spread
1 × 5ml spoon/1 teaspoon arrowroot
150g/5.3 oz natural yoghurt (1 small carton)
grated rind and juice of 1 lemon
liquid sweetener

Decoration
3 fresh apricots, stoned and halved

Soak the dried apricots in water overnight, then cook gently for 10 minutes in a little boiling water.

Rub together the flour and spread until the mixture resembles fine breadcrumbs. Add a little water and mix to form a soft dough. Roll out, and use the pastry to line a 20cm/8 inch flan ring. Leave in a refrigerator for at least 15 minutes. Bake the pastry case blind at 180°C/350°F/Gas 4 for 20 minutes.

Mix the arrowroot with with a little cold water and combine with the apricots, yoghurt, lemon rind and juice, and liquid sweetener. Pour into the pastry case and bake at 180°C/350°F/Gas 4 for a further 25 minutes. Decorate with the apricot halves.

Lime Baked Pears

SERVES 2

Total calories 100

2 large pears, peeled
2 cloves
150ml/$\frac{1}{4}$ pint low-calorie lime juice
liquid sweetener

Decoration
grated lemon rind

Cut the pears in half lengthways and put them in a deep ovenproof dish with the cloves and lime juice. Cover with foil and cook at 190°C/375°F/Gas 5 for 40 minutes. Remove the cloves, add the liquid sweetener and decorate with a little grated lemon rind.

Oaty Plum Pie

SERVES 4   *Total calories 840*

450g/1 lb dessert plums, stoned
liquid sweetener
100g/4 oz rolled oats
25g/1 oz sultanas
25g/1 oz wholewheat flakes (breakfast
  cereal)
1 × 5ml spoon/1 teaspoon nutmeg
1 size 3 egg, well beaten
150ml/¼ pint skimmed milk

Decoration
1 × 5ml spoon/1 teaspoon cinnamon

Put the plums and liquid sweetener in a large saucepan with a little cold water. Heat to boiling point, reduce the heat, cover and simmer for 10 minutes. Pour into an ovenproof dish. Mix the remaining ingredients together well and pour over the plums. Bake at 190°C/375°F/Gas 5 for 25 minutes. Sprinkle with cinnamon and serve hot.

Serving suggestion Natural yoghurt

Raspberry Curd Crumble

SERVES 4   *Total calories 340*

350g/12 oz raspberries
liquid sweetener
100g/4 oz curd cheese
50g/2 oz fresh wholemeal breadcrumbs
1 × 2.5ml spoon/½ teaspoon cinnamon
1 × 2.5ml spoon/½ teaspoon nutmeg

Put the raspberries in a bowl, add the liquid sweetener and fold in the curd cheese. Put the mixture into a 550ml/1 pint ovenproof dish, cover with breadcrumbs and sprinkle with cinnamon and nutmeg. Bake at 220°C/425°F/Gas 7 for 10 minutes. Serve hot or cold.

Blackcurrant Dessert (page 82), Mangoes and Strawberries (page 83),
Yoghurt Orange Ice (page 86) *and* Raspberry Curd Crumble (opposite)

Apricot Fluff

SERVES 2   *Total calories 120*

350g/12 oz fresh apricots *or* 50g/2 oz
  dried apricots, chopped
2 × 15ml spoons/2 tablespoons water
3 × 5ml spoons/3 teaspoons gelatine
2 egg whites

Cook the apricots in a little water until tender, then process in a blender. Put the water in a heatproof container, sprinkle in the gelatine and leave to soften. Stand the container in a pan of hot water and stir until the gelatine dissolves. Stir into the apricot purée. Whisk the egg whites until stiff and gently fold into the apricot mixture. Pour into two sundae glasses and leave in a refrigerator to set.

Blackcurrant Dessert

SERVES 4   *Total calories 180*

225g/8 oz blackcurrants
100g/4 oz cottage cheese
liquid sweetener
juice of $\frac{1}{2}$ lemon

Decoration
4 × 15ml spoons/4 tablespoons natural
  yoghurt
black grapes, halved
mint leaves

Steam the blackcurrants for about 10 minutes until tender. Stir in the cheese, sweetener and lemon juice. Sieve, or process in a blender. Pour into four glass dishes and chill in a refrigerator before serving. Put a spoonful of yoghurt in each glass dish, and decorate with a grape half and mint leaves.

Fruit Yoghurt Dessert

SERVES 4   *Total calories 220*

1 small grapefruit, peeled and cut into
  chunks
1 large orange, peeled and cut into
  chunks
1 medium apple, cored and sliced
1 medium pear, cored and sliced
150g/5.3 oz natural yoghurt (1 small
  carton)
liquid sweetener

Decoration
sliced strawberries

Mix the fruit together and gently fold in the yoghurt and liquid sweetener. Chill in a refrigerator, put the mixture into four glass dishes and decorate with sliced strawberries.

Mangoes and Strawberries

SERVES 4   *Total calories 160*

1 large mango, peeled, stoned and sliced
225g/8 oz strawberries, hulled and
  halved

Mix together the fruit and chill in a refrigerator. Serve in a glass dish.

Orange Apple Jelly

SERVES 4   *Total calories 280*

4 × 15ml spoons/4 tablespoons water
6 × 5ml spoons/6 teaspoons gelatine
150ml/$\frac{1}{4}$ pint unsweetened apple juice
275ml/$\frac{1}{2}$ pint unsweetened orange juice
150g/5.3 oz natural yoghurt (1 small
  carton)
liquid sweetener

Decoration
thin orange slices

Put the water in a heatproof container, sprinkle on the gelatine and leave to soften. Stand the container in a pan of hot water and stir until the gelatine dissolves. Mix together with the apple juice, orange juice, yoghurt and liquid sweetener. Pour into individual glass dishes and leave to set in a refrigerator. When set, decorate with orange slices.

Mandarin Cheesecake

SERVES 4–8   *Total calories 500*

25g/1 oz low fat spread
50g/2 oz wholewheat flakes (breakfast
  cereal)
2 × 15ml spoons/2 tablespoons water
3 × 5ml spoons/3 teaspoons gelatine
100g/4 oz curd cheese
1 × 225g/8 oz can mandarin oranges in
  natural juice
liquid sweetener

Decoration
orange segments
orange rind

Melt the low fat spread in a saucepan and stir in the wheat flake cereal. Press firmly on to the base of a 20cm/8 inch loose-bottomed cake tin and leave in a refrigerator to chill.

Put the water in a heatproof container, sprinkle in the gelatine and leave to soften. Stand the container in a pan of hot water and stir until the gelatine dissolves. Mix together with the curd cheese, mandarin oranges and liquid sweetener, and process in a blender. Pour on to the base and leave to set in a refrigerator. When set, decorate with a few orange segments and some orange rind.

Variation   *Total calories 680*
Use pineapple instead of mandarin oranges, and make the base with 50g/2 oz low fat spread and 75g/3 oz cereal. Use only 50g/2 oz curd cheese. Decorate with a little chopped pineapple.

Prune Delight

SERVES 2   *Total calories 180*

100g/4 oz stoned prunes
2 × 15ml spoons/2 tablespoons water
3 × 5ml spoons/3 teaspoons gelatine
vanilla essence
2 size 3 egg whites

Soak the prunes overnight in cold water. Drain, and put in a saucepan with sufficient boiling water to cover, and cook gently for 5 minutes. Sieve, or process in a blender. Put the water in a heatproof container, sprinkle in the gelatine and leave to soften. Stand the container in a pan of hot water and stir until the gelatine dissolves. Mix together with the prune purée and a few drops of vanilla essence. Whisk the egg whites until very stiff and gently fold into the prune mixture. Pour into two tall sundae glasses and leave to set in a refrigerator.

Mandarin Cheesecake

Pineapple Boats

SERVES 4   *Total calories 280*

1 medium pineapple
150g/5.3 oz natural yoghurt (1 small
   carton)
liquid sweetener

Cut the pineapple in half lengthways, scoop out and dice the flesh. Retaining a few pieces to use as a decoration, put the pineapple in a suitable container in a freezer, and leave until almost frozen. Remove from the freezer and mix with the yoghurt and liquid sweetener. Use to fill the pineapple shells and decorate with the reserved pineapple pieces. Serve immediately. Each half is shared between two people.

Yoghurt Orange Ice

SERVES 2   *Total calories 160*

150g/5.3 oz natural yoghurt (1 small
   carton)
200ml/7 fl oz unsweetened orange juice
   (1 small carton)
vanilla essence
orange food colouring

Decoration
fresh orange slices

Mix together the yoghurt, orange juice and a few drops of vanilla essence and food colouring. Put into a suitable container in a freezer and leave until partially frozen. Beat well, then freeze until firm. Serve with slices of fresh orange.

B·A·K·I·N·G

Following the principles of high fibre and less fat need not exclude the occasional baked item even when losing weight. This is because it is very much how and what you cook that is important rather than a blanket denial of baked products. Home-baked recipes can also be a useful way of introducing extra fibre into the diet, either as a main course or as a snack.

Almond, Coffee and Apple Layer Cake

SERVES 8

Total calories 860

50g/2 oz wholemeal/wholewheat flour
1 × 5ml spoon/1 teaspoon baking powder
1 × 5ml spoon/1 teaspoon instant coffee
2 × 15ml spoons/2 tablespoons boiling water
3 size 3 eggs, separated
50g/2 oz sugar
2 × 15ml spoons/2 tablespoons ground almonds

Filling
2 large eating apples, peeled, cored and sliced
liquid sweetener

Sift together the flour and baking powder. Dissolve the coffee in the water. Whisk the egg yolks and sugar until thick and creamy. Fold in the coffee, flour and ground almonds. Whisk the egg whites until stiff, and fold in carefully. Turn into a 20cm/8 inch greased and lined sandwich tin, and bake at 180°C/350°F/Gas 4 for 25 – 30 minutes.

Meanwhile, steam the apples until soft, then mash them and add the liquid sweetener. Leave to cool.

Split the sponge in half and fill with the apple mixture.

Orange Rind Cake

Total calories 880

50g/2 oz low fat spread
50g/2 oz sugar
2 size 3 eggs, well beaten
2 × 15ml spoons/2 tablespoons skimmed
 milk
100g/4 oz wholemeal/wholewheat flour
1 × 5ml spoon/1 teaspoon baking powder
grated rind of 2 oranges

Blend the low fat spread and sugar until light and creamy. Gradually add the egg and milk, beating well after each addition. Fold in the flour, baking powder and orange rind. Turn into a 450g/1 lb well greased loaf tin and bake at 180°C/350°F/Gas 4 for about 30 minutes until golden and springy to the touch.

Raisin Wheat Bread

Total calories 1350

175g/6 oz self-raising
 wholemeal/wholewheat flour
1 × 5ml spoon/1 teaspoon baking powder
50g/2 oz low fat spread
2 × 15ml spoons/2 tablespoons sugar
50g/2 oz wholewheat flakes (breakfast
 cereal)
50g/2 oz raisins
25g/1 oz currants
2 size 3 eggs, well beaten

Sift together the flour and baking powder, then rub in the low fat spread until the mixture resembles fine breadcrumbs. Add the sugar, cereal, raisins and currants, mix together well and bind with the beaten eggs. Put the mixture into a 450g/1 lb greased loaf tin and bake at 180°C/350°F/Gas 4 for about 30 minutes. Leave to cool before slicing.

Raisin Wheat Bread

Parmesan Wholemeal Scones

Total calories 800

100g/4 oz wholemeal/wholewheat flour
2 × 5ml spoons/2 teaspoons baking
   powder
1 × 2.5ml spoon/$\frac{1}{2}$ teaspoon salt
freshly ground black pepper
1 × 5ml spoon/1 teaspoon English
   mustard powder
50g/2 oz low fat spread
25g/1 oz Edam cheese, grated
25g/1 oz Parmesan cheese, grated
150ml/$\frac{1}{4}$ pint skimmed milk

Garnish
tomato wedges
sprigs of parsley

In a large bowl sift together the flour, baking powder, salt, pepper and mustard. Rub in the low fat spread until the mixture resembles fine breadcrumbs, then add the cheeses and milk and mix to a soft dough. Roll out on a lightly floured surface and use a pastry cutter to make eight scones. Put on to a baking sheet and bake at 230°C/450°F/Gas 8 for about 20 minutes until golden-brown. Garnish with tomato wedges and sprigs of parsley.

Yoghurt Wheat Scones

Total calories 480

100g/4 oz wholemeal/wholewheat flour
1 × 5ml spoon/1 teaspoon baking powder
25g/1 oz low fat spread
salt
150g/5.3 oz natural yoghurt (1 small
   carton)

Sift together the flour and baking powder in a large bowl. Rub in the low fat spread until the mixture resembles fine breadcrumbs. Stir in the salt and yoghurt and mix to form a soft dough. Roll out on to a lightly floured surface and use a pastry cutter to make eight scones. Put on a baking sheet and bake at 190°C/375°F/Gas 5 for 20 minutes until golden-brown. Serve hot.

Coconut Cheesecake

SERVES 4–8

Total calories 1440

75g/3 oz low fat spread
75g/3 oz wholewheat flakes (breakfast cereal)
6 digestive biscuits, crushed
2 size 3 eggs, separated
225g/8 oz cottage cheese
50g/2 oz desiccated coconut
1 × 15ml spoon/1 tablespoon skimmed milk
liquid sweetener

Melt the spread in a saucepan and stir in the cereal and crushed biscuits. Press the mixture on to the base of a 20cm/8 inch loose-bottomed cake tin. Beat the egg yolks together with the cottage cheese, coconut, milk and liquid sweetener. Whisk the egg whites until stiff and fold into the cheese mixture. Pour over the base and bake at 200°C/400°F/Gas 6 for 25 minutes until set and golden-brown. Serve hot or cold.

Oatcakes

Total calories 1080

25g/1 oz low fat spread
250g/9 oz oatmeal
$\frac{1}{2}$ × 2.5ml spoon/$\frac{1}{4}$ teaspoon salt
$\frac{1}{2}$ × 2.5ml spoon/$\frac{1}{4}$ teaspoon baking powder

Mix the low fat spread with a little boiling water. Add the remaining ingredients and mix to form a soft dough. Roll out thinly and cut into 12 portions. Put on to a baking sheet and bake at 190°C/375°F/Gas 5 for 25 minutes or until lightly coloured.

D·R·I·N·K·S

Drinks before or between meals can be very satisfying and real morale boosters, and some of those which follow will even convince you that you are not following a diet.

Chilled Coffee Cup

SERVES 2   *Total calories 120*

275ml/½ pint skimmed milk
1 × 15ml spoon/1 tablespoon instant
   coffee
liquid sweetener
6 ice cubes, crushed
grated cinnamon

Heat the milk gently, add the coffee and leave to dissolve, then cool. Add the liquid sweetener and crushed ice cubes, and serve in glasses with a little cinnamon sprinkled on the top.

Orange Strawberry Delight

SERVES 2   *Total calories 40*

juice of 1 lemon
75ml/⅛ pint natural orange juice
6 strawberries, hulled
550ml/1 pint cold water
liquid sweetener
6 ice cubes

Mix together the lemon juice, orange juice, strawberries, water and liquid sweetener. Sieve, or process in a blender, and pour into tall glasses with the ice cubes. Place a slice of lemon on the rim of each glass.

Decoration
lemon slices

At the back Orange and Grapefruit Cocktail (page 95) and Slimmer's Fruit
Punch (page 95), **At the front** Chilled Coffee Cup (opposite) *and* Crazy Cocktail (page 94)

Crazy Cocktail

SERVES 2   *Total calories 10*

75ml/⅛ pint sugar-free/low calorie bitter
  lemon
75ml/⅛ pint sugar-free/low calorie orange
150ml/¼ pint sugar-free/low calorie dry
  ginger
2 drops rum essence
ice cubes

Garnish
2 lemon slices
ground ginger (optional)

Mix together the bitter lemon, orange and dry
ginger with the rum essence and ice cubes. Chill in a
refrigerator, and serve in glasses with a lemon slice
in each. A little ground ginger can also be sprinkled
on the top.

Fluffy Chocolate Cup

SERVES 2   *Total calories 120*

425ml/¾ pint skimmed milk
4 drops chocolate essence
liquid sweetener

Heat the milk gently, then add the chocolate essence
and the liquid sweetener. Whisk until frothy and
serve immediately.

Iced Mint Tea

SERVES 2   *Total calories 10*

4 × 5ml spoons/4 teaspoons mint tea
  (4 sachets)
550ml/1 pint cold water
6 strawberries, hulled
liquid sweetener

Decoration
fresh mint leaves

Brew the mint tea using 550ml/1 pint water and
leave to cool. Remove the sachets, if used, and
transfer the tea to a glass jug. Add the strawberries
and sweetener, and leave in a refrigerator to chill.
Serve decorated with mint leaves.

Orange and Grapefruit Cocktail

SERVES 2   *Total calories 100*

150ml/¼ pint unsweetened orange juice
150ml/¼ pint unsweetened grapefruit
   juice
juice of 1 lemon
2 × 15ml spoons/2 tablespoons sugar-
   free/low calorie orange
150ml/¼ pint cold water
liquid sweetener
ice cubes (optional)

Decoration
sprigs of fresh mint
2 orange slices

Mix together the fruit juices, orange drink and water, and add the liquid sweetener. Fill cocktail glasses with ice cubes, if used, and pour in the juices. Decorate each glass with sprigs of mint and a slice of orange.

Slimmer's Fruit Punch

SERVES 2   *Total calories 20*

550ml/1 pint sugar-free/low calorie
   lemonade
2 lemon slices
2 orange slices
2 red-skinned apple slices
2 strawberries, hulled and sliced
4 cucumber slices
ice cubes

Decoration
sprigs of mint

Put the lemonade in a glass jug and add the fruit and cucumber slices. Chill in a refrigerator. Serve in glasses filled with ice cubes. Decorate with mint leaves.

I·N·D·E·X